Sacrifice

A legacy, a deadly bargain and a boy's mission

Oluyomi O'Tuminu

instant
ap□stle

First published in Great Britain in 2015

Instant Apostle
The Barn
1 Watford House Lane
Watford
Herts
WD17 1BJ

British Library Cataloguing-in-Publication Data

A catalogue record for this book is available from the British Library

This book and all other Instant Apostle books are available from Instant Apostle:

Website: www.instantapostle.com
E-mail: info@instantapostle.com

ISBN 978-1-909728-22-6

Printed in Great Britain

Everything that can be counted does not necessarily count; everything that counts cannot necessarily be counted.
Albert Einstein

Chapter one

6:43am Greenwich Meridian Time, 31st August 2022
The Kollay home, Cheriton, England
In the Third Dimension of the universe

Maseray was woken by the morning light streaming across her pillow. It was her birthday. She sat up in bed, yawned widely and fell back on the pillow. She grinned. She was alive.

She had been afraid to fall asleep last night and had decided to leave the heavy damask curtains in her bedroom open. If she was going to wake up the next morning, she did not want a jump-start from her alarm clock. Instead, she had wanted to be coaxed into consciousness by the rays of the early dawn. She'd dreaded nightfall and waited for her sons to go to bed before getting into her own. With the bedroom lights out, her eyes had adjusted to the moonlight which painted the walls silver and the furniture black. She'd dozed intermittently through the night, napping at short intervals. Eventually, her body overrode her will and she had drifted into a deep sleep.

For as long as she could remember, she had lived with the fear of dying young. None of the women on her mother's side of the family had ever lived past the age of 35. Evidently, she figured, that side of her family was cursed. But she'd faced a stone wall whenever she tried to talk to them about it. Her favourite aunt, Symchee, said,

'It's just a coincidence, darling. These things happen sometimes.'

Her mother's eldest sister's reply was, 'Ask your mother.'

Her mother's line was, 'You're too young to understand these things.'

By the time she was 18, Maseray had seen a dozen caskets containing the remains of her mother's relatives being lowered into their graves. Aunts, first cousins, second cousins... Every year, she would find herself at a funeral service, staring into the worn faces of her mother's relatives, assembled to pay their respects to the departed. She was usually unable to focus on any part of the service. She would feel guilty because she couldn't stop herself from scanning the crowd and wondering whose body would be lying in a coffin the next time they gathered.

Her mother was descended from a large family of prosperous merchants who had settled near Liverpool shortly before the Second World War. They had toiled hard and long to become successful diamond traders and had diversified into property ownership and estate development. When other businesses around them had fallen on hard times, the family business had found ways to flourish. Maseray's mother was born into luxury and she married well. By the time Maseray was born, the family was living in almost palatial surroundings in Gateacre, an affluent suburb near Liverpool. It was a friendly place with a strong sense of community.

At funerals and other gatherings, she would often hear sympathetic whispers among friends and neighbours expressing regret at the early demise of the women in her family. She'd hear them say, 'There are some things money cannot buy.' Maseray had come to expect the pitying looks and slick phrases intended to bring comfort to the bereaved.

When she turned nine, Maseray pressed her mother for an answer. 'I'm your only child. Your only daughter! Why can't you tell me?' Her mother reluctantly explained that things had always been that way in their family. No one really knew why. It had happened to her grandmother and her great-grandmother too. The answer was with Argoneo, the god of everything. He was the one who gave light with one hand and created darkness with the other. The things he had hidden from them were meant to remain a secret. Maseray concluded that the god of everything was cruel. What could be more important than life and death? If no one knew why things were the way they were, how could they stand a chance of fixing it?

Aunty Symchee, her mother's last surviving sister, died when Maseray was ten. The date was engraved on her memory: 29th April. It was a Tuesday and she was in school. At the beginning of a maths lesson mid-morning the headmistress walked in to fetch her. Her father was waiting outside the classroom. After they got into their car, her father told her that they were going to Aunty Symchee's house. 'Is she dead?' Her father nodded. 'Then the god of everything has failed me,' Maseray responded.

As they drove past the school gates, Maseray couldn't see through the blur of tears streaming down her face. Her mother was three years younger than Aunty Symchee. She was certain that in three years she would be at her mother's funeral, sitting in the front row at St

Michael of All Angels Church. She envisioned herself staring at Reverend Simon standing behind the pulpit and delivering his eulogy. Very little of it was likely to stick in her mind – not much he said ever did. She saw herself willing the service to come to an end so they could get through the burial part at the cemetery, the part that she hated the most.

Almost like clockwork, her premonition came true. Her mother died 33 months later, shortly before her thirty-fifth birthday. Much like any other night, her mother had tucked her into bed, kissed her softly and wished her sweet dreams. Maseray remembered feeling warm and cosseted as she fell asleep. When she woke up the next morning, it was to a quiet bustle in their home. She heard low voices and followed the sounds, walking down the corridor that led from her room to the kitchen. When she got there, she saw her father's brothers and their wives, her mother's cousin and her next-door neighbour. The digital clock on the window ledge said 8:23am. Maseray's heart began to race. *Why are all these people here at this time of the morning?*

'Where's Mum?'

Her father answered from behind her. 'Mum's not here.'

She turned around to face him. 'Is she dead?'

Her father knelt down in front of her. His eyes were welling up and she knew the answer even before he nodded. She screamed and clung to her father and continued to wail.

On the day of the funeral, Maseray was inconsolable, weeping bitterly for her beloved mother. For sweet Aunty Symchee. For herself. At the graveside, she passed out when her mother's coffin was being lowered into the grave. When she regained consciousness, she found herself in the back seat of their car with one of her uncles watching over her. It took her a moment to remember where she was. When Maseray realised she was at the cemetery, at her mother's burial, she put her hands to her face and wept once more.

As she had done many times before, she did the maths. She was certain that in about 20 years or so, her own family would witness this exact same scene at her own funeral. *Why? Why us?* She wiped her face with both hands and then wiped her hands on her black satin dress. *I want this to end. Let it end with me.* A possibility floated into her mind. Maseray held her breath and clenched her fists. Through her tears, she began to plead silently with the god of everything for two things: a husband like her father, and two children – only sons.

Now, she lay on her back staring up at the ceiling. Those were the thoughts of a broken-hearted little girl. Today she turned 35 and she had put childish things behind her. If the god of everything existed he had either forgotten about her or, thankfully, he was not interested in her. When her mother died she dealt with the pain of that loss and the loss of Aunty Symchee by putting them out of her mind. Something told her that she would snap if she tried to confront this grief head-on. She didn't have the strength for it.

When they'd got home after her mother's funeral, Maseray had inspected every room in the house and had taken down all of her mother's photographs and anything that she felt would remind her of her mother. She'd put all of the items in their guest bedroom. Her father had said nothing at the time because, she supposed, he expected this to be a temporary measure. He was probably sure that it was a knee-jerk reaction borne out of his daughter's grief. He had stood silently as Maseray ripped off the dress she'd worn to the funeral and shoved it in the kitchen bin.

In the weeks following, Maseray would clam shut whenever anyone talked about her mother. About Aunty Symchee. About the women on that side of her family. Her father did not prod her for an explanation. In time, the rest of her family followed suit and she guessed he had told everyone to leave her alone. Months later, when her father obviously realised that the items in the guest room were to remain there permanently, he took the trouble to arrange them neatly and to turn it into a small shrine in honour of his beloved wife. But Maseray never saw it: she would not step foot in that room.

Today of all days, I will not remember them. Maseray switched her thoughts to her husband, Cho. She smiled as she stretched her legs underneath the cotton sheet. She liked its smooth feel against her skin. Cho was an airline pilot and away at work. She and her sons were expecting him home in the afternoon. She suspected that as part of her birthday celebrations, Cho had made dinner reservations at their favourite Thai restaurant. She had certainly dropped enough hints. She rolled on to her side and stared out of the window. She was drained from not getting enough sleep, but she couldn't stop grinning. Why had she put herself through all that stress last night? Why worry about something if you can't change it? Que sera sera. From now on, she was going to savour every

9

moment, every hour, and take things one day at a time. Alive. She pulled the sheets up to her chin and rolled on to her back again. She giggled softly to herself. Her sons would be up in about an hour's time. She was going to stay in her room and wait patiently for them to surprise her with breakfast in bed.

Maseray dozed off again, and shortly after nine o'clock she was awakened by a thud on her door and her sons sauntering in, singing, 'Happy Birthday'. Kaithuli, her eldest, was carrying a large tray with a teapot, milk, sugar, cups and plates. Taifen was holding a smaller tray crammed with toast, jam, butter, cutlery and a birthday card. The boys put the trays down on the carpet. By now they were screeching the song and they broke into a dance. Taifen was bopping about like some kind of robot with a short circuit while Kaithuli seemed to be imitating a cowboy at a rodeo. Their song switched to a pop tune as they continued to prance around the room. Her eyes grew moist as she watched the boys. Their *joie de vivre* was infectious and she felt a surge of energy sweep through her body. Maseray sprang out of the bed, laughing, and joined the dance. Their joy gave her hope. For the first time in more than 25 years, she found the strength to believe that her fate might be different from all the women in her lineage.

◆ † ◆

Zacotan slipped the sheet of paper under the counter to the court clerk. He was a moneylender, and he had come to the Court Offices to register the judgment debt due to him. As he turned to walk away from the counter, the curtain parted and a woman stepped through it...

♦ † ♦

11:38am Greenwich Meridian Time, 31st August 2022
The Kollay home, Cheriton, England
In the Third Dimension of the universe

At precisely the same moment in time, 15-year-old Kaithuli let out a spine-chilling scream: 'Mum!' He was on the ground floor of the Kollay home, in the family games room, leaning over his mother. A few seconds ago, she had been locked against him in a fierce game of tennis on their Nacenvita Superdrive 50. Without warning, she had dropped her remote control and was clutching her chest as she fell forward onto the handwoven Berber carpet in the centre of the room.

'I... I... can't... breathe!' Maseray had gasped. 'I... I... uh!'

Kaithuli continued to play, returning the half-volley, his concentration focused on the 84-inch Sagamu Ultra 4D TV on the wall. Kaithuli's reasoning was that his mother, as usual, was fooling with him – it was match point and he was about to win in straight sets. She took a few more laboured breaths, but it was only when she began to spasm that Kaithuli realised this was no game. He dropped his remote control and immediately slid onto the floor, knees sinking into the woollen carpet as he bent over his mother. He turned her onto her back. She was motionless; her lifeless eyes stared directly ahead. Her mouth was still open and her chest stayed fully expanded from her final gasp for air.

Twelve-year-old Taifen watched, motionless. He had been lying cocooned in a beige leather beanbag which he had dragged to the centre of the games room. Watching the match between his mother and brother, he was the self-appointed commentator, delivering results in between mouthfuls of Pringles. As Maseray slumped to the floor, Taifen had also assumed that she was fooling around – a tactic designed to distract Kaithuli into losing the point. It was the vacant look in her eyes when Kaithuli placed their mother onto her back that made Taifen spring up from the beanbag, the Pringles tube sliding from his lap onto the carpet. By the time he reached his mother's side she had stopped breathing. Taifen squatted down, tapping his mother gently on her stomach.

'Mum, are you alright?'

'Tai, I want you to listen to me very carefully.' Kaithuli spoke slowly. His heart was pounding and he could feel his chest swelling as he took shorter gasps of breath. His eyes were already welling up.

'Taifen, I don't know what's wrong with Mum,' he said. There was a sense of foreboding in Kaithuli's voice and tears started to roll down his cheeks. Maseray Kollay was at the epicentre of their lives, coordinating the minutiae of their day-to-day living with complete devotion. Taifen raised his head and Kaithuli locked eyes with his younger brother. It wasn't just their mother who needed a miracle.

'Tai, you need to listen to me, OK?' Kaithuli pleaded. 'Mum's not feeling well and we need to help her. Our mobiles are upstairs and I'm going to stay with her so I need you to fetch the phone from the kitchen and bring it to me.'

Taifen flew out of the games room and raced down the marble-tiled hallway to the kitchen. He slammed open the large double oak doors and bounded in, heading towards the fridge. The kitchen lights switched themselves on automatically, growing from dim to full strength in an instant. Taifen could see that the phone was not on its base on the wall beside their enormous double-door refrigerator. He stopped and slowly cast his gaze around their pristine kitchen. Almost immediately, he spotted the white cordless phone on the granite-topped island in the centre of the kitchen. He grabbed it and sprinted back to the games room where his older brother was waiting. Taifen thrust the phone into Kaithuli's waiting palm.

'Great!' Kaithuli spoke in an encouraging tone. 'Now just sit nicely. We need to be brave, OK?' Taifen nodded and knelt over his mother with his knees lightly touching the crown of her head. He brushed his tears away, then placed his trembling palms on her shoulders and began to whisper in a strange multi-syllabic tongue: *'Reho sebo roma, testrei, meli-tera-peli-terum. Kiro…'*

Kaithuli had already dialled 999 and was waiting for a response. On the second ring a voice answered.

'Hello, Emergency Services. Do you require police, ambulance or fire and rescue?'

Kaithuli's voice quivered. 'My mum's just collapsed and she's not breathing. Please send an ambulance: she needs help fast!'

'Thank you,' the operator responded. 'Please hold while I connect you.'

Kaithuli could feel sweat break above his upper lip. It felt like the emergency services were wasting precious time.

'This is the Ambulance Emergency Services. I understand that your mother has just collapsed?'

'Yes, that's what I just said, you need to send an ambulance now, right away – she's not breathing and she's not moving!' Kaithuli responded, his voice rising with agitation.

'What is your name, please?' the new operator asked; it was a male voice this time.

'My name is Kaithuli Kollay. I live at number 7 Foxfield Lane, Cheriton, London. You need to send an ambulance right away, right now! My mum needs help!'

Terror was no longer just gnawing at Kaithuli's belly; he could feel it rapidly ascending from his gut to his chest, seeking to stifle the air in his lungs. Out of the corner of his eye, Kaithuli thought he saw a dark figure sprint from the left side of the room across to the right corner next to the antique lampstand. But when he turned his head to look, his eyes saw no one, nothing. Yet it felt like someone or something was crouching there.

The lamp was five feet tall, made from solid ebony and carved in the shape of Shenge, the African goddess of light. Her almond-shaped eyes and full lips were breathtaking against the flawless canvas of her polished dark skin. In the place where her tummy would have been, a hollow space was carved to hold the lamp's bulb. It had been a birthday gift to their mum from one of her maternal cousins when she turned 30. Their father had never liked the lamp. He said it was stunning but carried a strange aura and he refused to have it in their bedroom. Their mother had teased him about it, and as a compromise Shenge was allowed to occupy a corner of the games room.

Shenge almost seemed to be smiling. Kaithuli stared momentarily, for she had always appeared expressionless before.

'Kaithuli, are you there?' the operator interrupted his thoughts. He was clearly overwhelmed and his mind was playing tricks on him.

'Kaithuli, are you still there?'

The question triggered a torrent of red-hot anger within him and Kaithuli felt like screaming at the voice on the other end of the phone. The operator was wasting valuable time. The paramedics should already be making their way to his house to save his mother's life. He wanted to slap the operator, to scream and curse at him. Instead, it was the pitiful sobs of a helpless young boy that emerged from his lips as he began to weep softly.

'Kaithuli, I know this is difficult but I need you to stay with me if we are going to help your mother,' the operator encouraged. 'Are there any other adults with you in the…?'

The phone slipped from Kaithuli's grip as he pulled his knees up to his head and his body assumed a rocking motion. He could no longer bear to look at his mother lying motionless before him, and his mind refused to accept what his eyes reported. Maybe this was a dream, a nasty reverie, and he would awaken at any moment to put this horrific nightmare behind him. A couple of hours ago, he and Taifen had been leaping around in their parents' bedroom. Their mother had joined in with them, hugging and kissing them, joining in their dance. Even after they had washed and dressed, all three were still in high spirits and they had headed to their family games room for some computer gaming before lunch.

Kaithuli tried to go over in his mind again everything that had happened that morning, but it felt like his brain had frozen and was refusing to work. How had they gone from sharing the joy in their mother's eyes to staring at her lifeless body? As he rocked back and forth, Kaithuli's chest heaved in an unsteady, erratic rhythm. Their mother was gone and he succumbed to an overwhelming feeling of powerlessness. As he let it wash over him, he hugged his knees tightly to his chest. He could no longer suppress the muffled sounds of pain spilling from his lips as he sobbed uncontrollably. There was no magic that could bring his mother back, but he had to do something. He knew he needed to steady himself to think clearly.

From what he had learned at school about the origins of life in the universe, Kaithuli had concluded that there was a scientific explanation for everything. If something could not be perceived with the five senses or could not be proven by scientific testing, then he reasoned that it could not be true. He had had many heated discussions with his father who felt otherwise and was convinced that there was a supreme power ruling the universe and life beyond the grave. Increasingly over the last year, Kaithuli had been having similar debates with Taifen, who had accepted their dad's points of view. He would regularly have arguments with his younger brother on the existence of higher powers and life beyond the physical realm.

So Kaithuli had no rational explanation for what he did next. Yet it was something that almost every desperate soul does in the face of despair. He began to plead with an unknown god.

'I don't know if you exist. I don't know if I believe in you. But if you are real and if you are really out there, help us! Let our mum come back to us! Let her live. Please let my mum live.'

♦ † ♦

11:38am Greenwich Meridian Time, 31st August 2022
En route from Cheriton, England, to the First Dimension, the
Dark Soul of the universe

During my life on Earth, I had been neither hot nor cold about anything. When I died, I knew instinctively that I had stepped out of time into another dimension. My senses immediately made me aware that I was in grave danger, but from what? I was travelling somewhere at an incredible speed, feet first and vertically down through what felt like a cylindrical corridor where the temperature was rising. It felt like I was being dragged down towards the bowels of the Earth. My immediate reaction was to struggle against this unseen yet irresistibly powerful current which was sucking me downwards. I fought with every ounce of strength to swim back up, but I couldn't. The force was too strong, almost magnetic, and it kept pulling me down the tunnel.

A bizarre thought floated into my head: I was heading for the Earth's core. My response was an overwhelming desire to return to the comfort of my life in Cheriton, a sleepy suburb on the outskirts of London. I just wanted to slip back into my humdrum daily existence. With this longing, my mind started to fill with images of my sons, Kaithuli and Taifen. Then of Cho, my first and only love, high-school sweetheart, best friend and husband.

As my mind raced on, the images of my family were substituted with that of a middle-aged man whom I had watched on Eclipse TV, one of the many satellite broadcasting channels. I remembered a man giving his account of an out-of-body encounter that he had experienced on a hospital operating table. He was a maths professor, slightly balding, with a large head and deep-set blue eyes. He was stocky but not overweight, and although not conventionally attractive he had kind, soulful eyes that demanded the viewer's attention.

As the maths professor spoke, he explained that on the day in question, he had been feeling unwell and was admitted into hospital for some tests. Unfortunately, within hours of checking into the hospital and even before his test results were returned, he suffered a pulmonary embolism – a blood clot in his lungs. He described how he had slowly suffocated to death and had eventually taken his final breath lying on a hospital bed. He said that in an instant, it was as though his entire life unfolded before him. It was like watching a movie that displayed all the key events of his life with supreme clarity. He described being in some kind of hyperspace dimension beyond the Earth, where he knew that he was dead and that time had stopped. Yet he was also aware of what was happening to his body on the hospital bed and the fuss being made by the doctors and nurses.

I remembered that as I was listening to the professor's tale, I believed every word. I was not sure whether it was the warmth in his eyes or the serenity he exuded, but I accepted his story as fact. So as I sped down the narrow chute, I was baffled. Why was I not witnessing a movie of the key events in my own life? When the professor died, he was transported to a peaceful place and en route he had experienced waves of a magnificent, shimmering light. In my case, there was no light anywhere. As I sped through this corridor, I was surrounded by a thick blackness that my eyes were powerless to penetrate. It was getting hotter and I was beginning to feel nauseous. Even though I could not see any part of my body, I knew that I was drenched in sweat. I was suffocating from the dry heat, and tasted bile in my mouth. I began to retch.

'Maseray Kollay, you are a daughter of the Sekou bloodline. You have arrived in the First Dimension of the universe. This is the Region of the Vanquished,' a slurred voice announced in an almost deafening tone as I crashed into hard ground. 'You are here because as a daughter of the Sekou bloodline you have been judged as vanquished. You are here to carry out your sentence!'

My mind was spinning, and as waves of terror washed over my body, I tried to run. But my legs would not function. Betrayed by my own feet, I crumpled into a heap on the floor. As I lay there, doors slid open and for the first time since my peculiar journey began, I could see. I was lying by what seemed to be a portal. I looked up and my eyes fell upon a large figure wearing a silver crown, lavishly decorated with tiny diamonds and with a large sapphire as its centrepiece. I was struck by his honey-gold complexion and blue-black eyes set in a sweet oval face. He was a young man, about six feet tall with almost cherubic features. His red-gold gleaming locks fell to his waist. He was sporting a silver breastplate that emitted soft blue-gold rays of light which illuminated our surroundings. He flicked a strand of stray hair off his face with a perfectly manicured hand, placing it behind his ear.

'Where am I...? Wow, you're beautiful!' I gasped, momentarily distracted by the creature's dazzling beauty. Scarcely had these words left my lips when the creature morphed before my very eyes.

'Used to be!' he snarled. 'I used to be – beautiful. But now it's just a neat little trick I use to welcome new arrivals.'

I was now staring into the yellow slits of the huge bulging eyes of what looked like a giant grasshopper. Its head was jet black and sat on top of its disproportionately long, scaly neck. I forgot to breathe. The pounding sound of my heart racing crowded out all thoughts in my head as the skin on my arms and legs turned to gooseflesh. The creature stood almost two and a half metres tall and had the body of a horse. Its coarse black coat was moulting, leaving large bald patches on its body. It had thick scaly limbs which ended in coal-black twisted talons, and there were six huge black wings neatly folded on its back. The diamond-encrusted silver crown now sat ignominiously between the two short, stumpy antennae protruding from its head.

'Stand up and follow me. I am Balak, a gatekeeper here in the First Dimension of the universe. I will lead you to the holding area and to the new arrivals check-in desk, where your details will be verified to ensure that there is a sealed judgment against you and that your name is duly recorded in the *Book of the Vanquished*. Thereafter you will be handed over to the chief sentry of the penitentiary for your final incarceration.'

As I rose to follow Balak along the narrow corridor, my befuddled senses attuned to the blood-curdling screams coming from somewhere deep within this place I was being taken to. Whoever they were, they could only be in the most excruciating pain as their futile pleas for mercy went unheeded. I shuddered to think that shortly, I, Maseray Kollay, wife, and mother of two sons, was shortly to be incarcerated in some kind of prison. But why? For the first time in more than 20 years, overcome by fear, I found myself whispering, 'Argoneo, help me!'

Balak was instantly catapulted into the air by an unseen force and hurled violently against the corridor wall. He slid slowly onto the floor, completely winded and visibly in great pain. As he fought to regain his composure, he bared huge yellow fangs at me and said, almost inaudibly, 'You must never mention that name here again – this is your final warning. Next time you will be immediately summoned by the Dragon. I can assure you that you are not ready to make his acquaintance.'

'The Dragon?' I gasped.

'Yes, the Dragon, Zacotan.'

Speechless at his reply, I simply nodded my head in acknowledgment and shuffled on. Was it my imagination, or had I momentarily glimpsed terror on the face of my escort? I shuddered involuntarily, and as I did so I reminded myself that I did not have the luxury of time for any further analysis. Presently, I was facing the prospect that very soon my own voice would swell the sickening chorus of ear-splitting shrieks resonating from within the bowels of this wholly unnerving place.

Balak and I arrived at the end of the narrow corridor where the doors automatically opened into a gigantic room which I assumed to be the holding area. The room was dimly lit by the glow emanating from many large diamonds embedded in the low ceiling. The diamonds were the size of tennis balls and seemed to contain the dying embers of a fire. As I peered ahead, there was a sea of heads with innumerable queues of thousands of people waiting in line.

'Join a queue – any one will do,' Balak sniggered. 'You need to check in at an arrivals desk. The computers are all fully updated. They will have your name and the record of your election of Zacotan as your idol. You will receive a micro-certificate of your conviction from the Court of the Tenth Dimension. It will contain the details of the judgment recorded against you in the *Book of the Vanquished*. You will also receive information about your prison sentence here in the penitentiary. Check in, and the fun begins! No hurry, of course – you have for ever!' Balak threw his head back and roared at his joke before continuing, 'All beings, whether human or not, whose names are not registered in the *Book of the Acquitted*, are to be confined to the core of the First Dimension of the universe. Great weather – you'll love it. The First Dimension is a space within the Earth's core. The actual penitentiary is made of liquid magma, a mesmerising molten ocean called the Sea of Volcanus. We also fondly call it the "Fiery Sea",' Balak snorted gleefully.

'What? I mean, I don't understand.'

'Shut up!' Balak retorted savagely as he bent down, lowering his face so that he and I were eye to eye. I started to shake and I wrapped my arms tightly around myself, clutching my sides, hoping to control the quaking. I closed my eyes, yet even so I could feel the intensity of his hateful gaze.

'As I was saying,' Balak pulled himself up and continued slowly and deliberately. 'You are now in the First Dimension of the universe which lacks the element of time but has plenty of space. When it was designed, time was completely omitted. That is why life here in Volcanus is for *for ever!*'

With that, Balak the gatekeeper vanished.

I glanced around the holding chamber, astonished at the sheer size of this room that contained the largest gathering of people I had ever seen. I had been to a few music concerts in the recent past, including the *Food of Love 2020* concert, a fundraiser for cancer research. It had been held in the English countryside and the organisers hosted around a million fans over a long weekend. Here in the holding chamber, I gasped as my eyes surveyed the space. I was completely unprepared to see such a huge throng of bodies, especially after what had so far been a solitary journey. Where did all these people come from? Were they dead? Was I dead? I started to panic.

The room was eerily quiet and yet its hush was frequently punctuated by sour shrieks and yelps. Then there was the smell – a horrible pungent stench. My throat started to close and at the same time I felt the bile making its way up through my chest. I could no longer push it back and I opened my mouth expecting to vomit. Instead, a few drops of saliva slid out and then I belched loudly. Embarrassed, I slowly scanned my section of the room. I noticed that most people faced forward. Those who turned to look at me seemed reluctant to make eye contact. Others looked down at their feet. Like automatons, each one shuffled along in their respective queue. Besides the shrill whelps, no one spoke. Very few seemed to peer around like I was. Was it possible to escape from this place? And if I tried to run, where would I go?

I could feel heat rising beneath my feet. I stepped forward and fell over, face forward. The ground was constructed from translucent green-black crystal tiles. A fiery glow shone through the tiles from what appeared to be a reddish-gold molten fluid running beneath its surface. It was only then that I noticed the rings of translucent bronze that chained my feet together.

'You there, get up and join a queue before I make you!' came a thin and raspy warning voice from behind me.

I was too petrified to search out the voice's owner. I pulled myself up and slid into the nearest queue. I looked back and realised that the number of bodies arriving behind me was growing constantly. A matter of seconds after I had entered the holding area I could no longer see the end of my queue.

Everything was totally perplexing. When had the bronze rings been placed on my feet? I was now fully ensconced in a moving queue and obliged to keep moving ahead. My mind was swirling with questions. In my disorientated state, I stretched my neck so I could see what was happening at the front. I noticed that there were guards patrolling the wide aisles between each column of people. The guards looked identical to Balak, each with the head of a giant black grasshopper, a long scaly neck, six huge black scaly wings and the body of a horse. Except now I saw that these winged monsters also had tails... which were snakes. My pulse spiked. Were Balak and these guards some kind of extraterrestrial beings? As they moved along the aisles, their tails would swish about and the snake heads would lunge fiercely at anyone within reach. Whenever a snake head succeeded in biting someone, there was a piercing cry of raw pain from the victim as the snake's fangs ripped through their flesh, followed by pathetic whimpers. I was going to have to watch out for those tails or snakes or whatever they were.

I looked ahead and saw that our column was leading up to a check-in desk. In fact, there were multiple check-in desks running along the front of the chamber. Each column had a dedicated check-in desk, and suspended overhead, above each one, was a large, flat, rectangular, digital screen. There was a message in red lights scrolling along the screen but I was not close enough to read it. I was not too concerned about the message at this point; one thing at a time. Right now, it was more important to keep watch for approaching guards and their tails. I was listening keenly for the shrieks of the snake-bitten victims so I could judge how near a guard was to me.

As the queue slowly inched towards our desk, I was finally able to decipher the writing on the digital screen. The message scrolled in red lights:

```
In the First Dimension of the universe,
 check-in desk for convicts sentenced to
    LIFE IMPRISONMENT without parole.
```

Chapter two

Nurishad sat in a glass cubicle on the twelfth floor in the east wing of the Gallery of Histories. History was his favourite subject and he adored the elegant surroundings of this particular gallery with its lofty ceilings, warm airy feel and pleasant lighting. Its walls were made of translucent crystal, and the building sat suspended some 30 metres above a lush emerald-green lake that was home to schools of brightly coloured fish.

Whenever he visited, Nurishad could easily spend hours in the quiet of the gallery, without food or drink, scrolling through reams of ancient texts on any topic. But his passion was to study the origins of the universe. He never grew tired of reading around this subject. He was a lawyer in the Court of the Tenth Dimension and extremely devoted to his work. Today, however, was Nurishad's rest day and he planned to enjoy himself. Technically, he was on standby duty and could be called to work at any time, but unless he was recalled, he was going to spend the day in the Gallery flicking through writings on his favourite subject: *The Chronicles of Beings: Celestial and Terrestrial.*

Above the desk in the small cubicle was a cuboid digital screen that was suspended in mid-air. As he pushed his chair into the curve of the desk, the screen lowered automatically and adjusted itself to Nurishad's eye level. A built-in camera scanned his iris. All the computers in the Gallery were activated using a biometric data system of iris recognition and fingerprinting. Nurishad leaned forward, spun the cuboid slowly and held it stationary on its third revolution. Then he placed his index finger on the glowing amethyst button at the bottom of the screen.

'Please confirm your identification credentials.'

'Nurishad the Noble, Special Advocate, Mount of Assembly, Tenth Dimension.'

The screen widened, bringing up more than 100 glowing icons, evenly arranged in tidy rows and columns.

'Welcome, Nurishad. You have clearance to access all files archived in the Gallery of Histories save those restricted to members of the Supreme High Council.'

Nurishad's index finger hovered over the screen. He slid it slowly along the rows and stopped at the sixth row of the ninth column, clicking on the icon named 'The Battle of Primary Chaos'. He skipped past the table of contents and went straight to the main chapters:

The Celestial Age – The Battle of Primary Chaos
Three million years before the Age of Terrestrial Beings, there was war in the Tenth Dimension. This was the first war anywhere in the universe; a rebellion against Argoneo, Lord of the universe, instigated by his first underlord, Zacotan. It is known as 'The Battle of Primary Chaos'. At that time there was only one law in the universe: to do the bidding of the Supreme High Council. In turn, the Council ascribed powers of

authority to Argoneo, giving him dominion to rule as Lord of the universe.

Argoneo was a just and noble potentate, gracious and kind. He had chosen Zacotan to rule as the first of three underlords reporting directly to him. But Zacotan proved to be disloyal and corrupt and attempted to overthrow his master's rule.

Nurishad clicked the page shut. He scrolled along the screen and clicked on another icon containing more information on 'Origins of the Celestial Age', and then skipped to the fourth paragraph of the third chapter. His home was in the Mount of Assembly in the City of the Sacred Mountain, and he loved to read about its genesis.

Annal 3(iv) – The Palace of Assembly

During the construction process of the revealed universe, Argoneo decided to build his home in the heart of the Tenth Dimension, which is the centre of the revealed universe. The exact spot is found high above the Great Siyon which is the tallest mountain in the Tenth Dimension. There, he constructed a colossal palace in the form of an open-faced cube suspended 12,000 metres above the mountain's peak. This cube is surrounded by a range of seven huge mountains forming a semicircle around it. Argoneo named this floating mountain range the Sacred Mountain; the palace he called the Mount of Assembly.

The palace grounds are extensive and contain many gardens bursting with all kinds of flower and fruit trees, bushes and plants. It is a riot of colours and sweet fragrances with delectable fruits and berries ripe for picking. A river runs at a steady pace through the City of the Sacred Mountain, flowing from a source within the Palace …

Annal 3(vi) – The Dawn of Celestial Beings

At the dawn of time, the universe was shapeless, empty and condensed. Argoneo, a celestial being without beginning or end of days, summoned a meeting of his peers in the Supreme High Council. By unanimous vote, Argoneo was granted the title deeds to the entire universe.

After a period of deep contemplation, Argoneo designed and constructed the celestial bodies – planets, suns, moons and stars. After this work was completed, Argoneo turned to the next task on his agenda, which was the designing and birthing of celestial beings. This proved to be a painstaking process because it involved the partial cloning of Argoneo's own cells. Argoneo engineered and spawned tens of dozens of prototypes for celestial creatures. He used the prototypes to generate more than ten million creatures. These beings were classified into different categories, and the difference in their design was linked to their function. Yet they all had something in common. They were hyper-dimensional beings, unconstrained by time and space, born never to die.

Argoneo dispersed these creatures throughout the Fifth to the Ninth Dimensions of the universe as their homes. Yet they were granted the freedom to travel to all regions in all ten Dimensions of the universe. There was no division between the visible and the invisible worlds because everything was perfect and in perfect order. Celestials shared a common language but also had many local dialects spoken within the regions where they lived. These creatures lived in complete harmony within all ten Dimensions of the cosmos; there was no fear, hatred or violence anywhere in the universe.

◆ † ◆

'Se ro mo sirimi malakari ti ro ki...' Kaithuli's thoughts swung to the sound of his brother's voice. Taifen continued to lean over their dead mother. Both his hands were now gently touching her chest; the tone of his voice had switched from a soothing sound to that of a militant cadence. Kaithuli stretched his legs out in front of him and sat with hunched shoulders next to his mother's body. He desperately longed for his father. But at that moment Cho Kollay was 10,000 metres in the air over the Atlantic Ocean. His mobile phone was dutifully switched off as he piloted the 747 jet towards its intended destination – Heathrow Airport – for its scheduled landing in 56 minutes. Even if Kaithuli left a voicemail message asking for help, his father would not listen to it for at least another hour. And right now, they could not spare 60 seconds, let alone 60 minutes.

'Herith sefa kirith meroti saremith kothobothi...' Taifen had launched into another verse of gibberish, his voice growing louder and more authoritative. It was a peculiar language. *'Kara beli tehemo shebozo... re he maksa-le...'*

Taifen's even tone helped to steer Kaithuli's focus on the grim reality of the situation. Next to him, his brother was spouting nonsense while their mother lay motionless on the carpet. Their father was hundreds of metres high up in the sky. And the emergency services were playing the fool. Kaithuli hurriedly wiped away the tears rolling down his cheeks and blinked rapidly. He shook his head roughly from side to side, trying to shake off the fogginess in his mind to prevent it playing more tricks on him.

As he fixed his gaze upon Taifen, it appeared as though his brother's hands were on fire. Taifen's small hands, which were still resting on their mother's chest, now seemed to be immersed in a steady white-hot fire, but neither his mother's blouse nor Taifen's hands were burning. He was now sitting silently, appearing almost statuesque as he stared ahead at the wall. His eyes were unblinking and his face was expressionless. Kaithuli waved a hand in front of his brother's face. Taifen's eyes remained unblinking.

Dad help us, we need you! Kaithuli cried silently. *Mum is dead, Taifen is in shock and the grief is making me crazy.*

Chapter three

11:40am Greenwich Meridian Time, 31st August 2022
Somewhere over the Atlantic Ocean, en route to Heathrow
Airport, London

Cho Kollay looked down at the growing circles of sweat on the armpits of his shirt. His temples were throbbing and now the dull ache at the base of his neck was creeping out along his shoulders. He didn't know what to make of this sudden discomfort. He had slept soundly the previous night and he'd woken up feeling vibrant. He was returning home to London today and had floated out of bed in his hotel room, then stepped into a warm shower where he'd soaped and scrubbed all over while singing Michael Jackson's 'Billie Jean' rowdily in a falsetto voice. His sons would often call him an old-timer and tease him about his love of outdated music. It was Maseray's birthday and he couldn't wait to get home to serenade her. The thought of dinner at the Oasis of Shangri La tonight with her and the boys made him giddy.

Initially, when his head had begun to ache, he had assumed it was a tension headache. Through his years of experience as a commercial pilot it was usually his *inner pilot* warning him about some mechanical or other failure with the aircraft – which was currently on autopilot. He had immediately awakened his sleeping co-pilot, Andy Jaggar, and ordered a thorough examination of the aircraft – its engine, the wings, the fuel gauge and even the passenger manifest. Everything had proved to be completely satisfactory. After the second round of inspections had failed to detect any faults with the aircraft, Andy had grudgingly participated in the third round. He had made it clear to Cho that he wanted to go back to sleep. Cho felt too embarrassed to insist on anything else after that. Even so, he was not able to slow his racing heart.

The aircraft was fine so he scrolled through a mental checklist of possibilities. His wife and sons were safe and well. At that very moment, they were safely ensconced in the large six-bedroomed detached house on the outskirts of London that he had toiled diligently to acquire. Maseray was an art lover and their home was dotted with exquisite paintings and sculptures amid the specially commissioned furniture chosen to complement the artwork. Cho was a gadget man and usually found it hard to resist appliances, computers or tools which were cutting edge and well designed. The large oak shed at the end of their 90-metre garden was mostly a depot for not-so-new gadgets that had been retired early and awaited transportation to friends or local charities. At this time of the day, he expected the family to be relaxing in the cinema room watching a movie or perhaps in the games room playing pool, table tennis or Nacenvita Superdrive 50 games.

Cho was an exceptional pilot, and over the past 18 years he had enjoyed an outstanding career. He checked the monitors on the cockpit again, his eyes scouring the panels for the slightest indication of any anomaly. There was nothing; the flight was progressing as it should.

Cho's mind computed that there was no need for apprehension but his pulse was racing, and now he was sweating and shivering at the same time.

'The paradox of a fever,' he muttered to himself as he reached for his pullover and dragged it over his head. 'I am the captain of this ship and all is well. I am the captain of this ship and all is well. I am the captain and... and...' Cho swallowed deeply to keep the sobs at bay. His cheeks were wet and he reached inside his trouser pocket for his handkerchief. As he dried his face, he glanced over at Andy, slumbering peacefully in his seat. He envied him, because he could not shake off the ominous feeling entwining his gut.

To calm his nerves, he began to whisper a tune that his old nanny had taught him when he was about six. It had been so long ago that Cho struggled to remember the words, but the melody leapt up in his heart so he kept singing while he reached for the words. They came slowly at first and so he sang haltingly under his breath, skipping words but staying with the melody. He remembered part of a verse and then the chorus, and then the song swam fully back into his head. He continued to sing.

Cho was glad Andy was asleep. He didn't want to have to explain to him why he was so restless or why he felt compelled to sing a childish ditty to soothe his anxiety.

◆ † ◆

11:41am Greenwich Meridian Time, 31st August 2022
The Jos family home, Gateacre, Liverpool, UK
In the Third Dimension of the universe

Since Maseray had turned 30, her father found that he always had trouble sleeping the night before her birthday. He would fret during the week leading up to it, and the night before it would be particularly difficult. It was not something Joseph Jos felt he could discuss with his daughter so he kept his worries to himself. He had almost become resigned to the ill fortune that seemed to prescribe an early death for the women on his late wife's side of the family. It seemed unstoppable, and his wife's death had dealt a devastating blow to him.

As a young man, before he had married her, Joseph had heard the rumours and conjecture surrounding Monisola's family. Some people had said that her family was cursed. When they started their courtship, Joseph's parents discussed with him the rumours they had heard, in particular their concerns about a curse. He dismissed their remarks because he had loved Monisola from the moment he set eyes on her. He was captivated by her gentle eyes and shy smile. Maseray had the same eyes.

Joseph's parents had been reluctant to give their blessing to their marriage. To appease his father, he had persuaded Monisola to take a series of medical examinations. She had passed all the checks and was declared to be in an excellent state of health. So his parents had given their blessing, and their wedding day had been a happy one. They did not have to wait too long before Maseray arrived.

Joseph closed his eyes. He couldn't bear to think that he would lose Maseray, his only child. It was unnatural: a father should never have to bury his daughter.

Even though Joseph had been up since dawn, he did not want to wake Maseray so had waited until mid-morning to call her to wish her a happy birthday. To his relief, she had answered the phone and they'd chatted briefly. Joseph was elated to hear her voice and had tried to mask his feelings by being chirpy, but instead he had sounded overly cheerful. He'd also spoken to his grandsons.

He put the phone down, reminded of how fortunate he was to have such lovable grandchildren. He also realised how hungry he was and reached for the intercom at his bedside to call his housekeeper. He told her that he was ready for a large breakfast. She had obliged with freshly squeezed orange juice and a plate full of scrambled eggs, muffins and tomatoes, and a bowl of his favourite – blueberries. Joseph's stomach was loaded as he crawled under his duvet to nap. His eyes felt weighted and his sluggish body was calling for slumber.

Just before he drifted off to sleep, he had an urge to call a friend, Lillian, to talk to her about his fears regarding the *curse*. Lillian lived in one of the neighbouring villages and they'd met many years ago at Cho and Maseray's wedding. Since that time, Joseph had come across her occasionally at family celebrations.

Lillian was sweet tempered and softly spoken. Joseph enjoyed her company although he could not say entirely why he felt so comfortable around her. Maybe it was the way she spoke – it was as though she chose each word thoughtfully, like some rare stock under ration, before letting it roll off her tongue. Even when she ventured on subjects that they disagreed on – like life beyond the Earth and invisible worlds within our world – he was drawn to listen to her. Regardless of whether Lillian was right about those things, he was going to call her. He needed to speak to someone about this issue that had plagued him over the last quarter of a century.

Chapter four

Nurishad had already spent an hour in the Gallery of Histories. He smiled as he scrolled down the screen, skipping several more pages in *The Chronicles of Beings: Celestial and Terrestrial*. Although he had memorised the next few passages and knew them off by heart, he always got a thrill from reading the text on the screen.

Annal 6 – Celestial Life Before the Birth of the Dragon at The Battle of Primary Chaos

The birthing of the Dragon took place at The Battle of Primary Chaos. Before this inglorious event, there was no division between the visible and the invisible worlds. Life in the universe flowed in complete harmony. There was a constant stream of movement between all ten Dimensions. Celestial creatures were able to travel through hyperspace and were continuously ascending and descending through the special portals designed for free movement in the universe.

Celestials were a highly organised society of individuals, each one graced with intelligence, equipped for a specific purpose and fitted with a key assignment. There were artists, architects, engineers, chefs, musicians, dancers, craftsmen, astronomers, and many more. They wanted for nothing and were engaged in all manner of scientific and scholastic endeavours.

At Argoneo's invitation, some celestial dwellers migrated to the Tenth Dimension and this conurbation grew into what is the City of the Sacred Mountain. From among this group of celestials, an elite squad was selected and personally tutored by Argoneo to work with him in the Palace of Assembly. Argoneo equipped these chosen few with many skills. One such skill was the mastery of a unique celestial language known only to each other and to him. Since that time no other celestials have been taught this language.

♦ † ♦

11:41am Greenwich Meridian Time, 31st August 2022
The Kollay home, Cheriton, England
In the Third Dimension of the universe

'Simiri ko-lu-me rositma ti-ko-ro, parra o semo lema kara, Tefleo negero beli bela…' With eyes closed and both hands still on his mother's chest, Taifen dutifully chanted on in the unknown language. He had first started to speak this language last year. To be precise, it was on 5th September 2021, the day after his twelfth birthday.

That September morning, after breakfast, Cho Kollay had gone directly to Taifen's bedroom. It was his intention to speak to Taifen about the meaning of life. Indeed, Cho's discussion with Taifen was timely because he did not know that Taifen was already traversing the barrier between the visible and invisible worlds. In his dreams, Taifen was being schooled by mystical visitors. They were showing him how to slip into the unseen realms of the universe. The visitors were pleased with Taifen and the ease with which he was able to access the invisible world. Taifen was already treading beyond his depth. With a little more grooming, the visitors would seek to draw him to the Dark Soul of the universe.

The grooming process had started in quite an ordinary fashion. Taifen was an outstanding pupil. He revelled in the praise lavished upon him at home and at school. Without exception, Taifen excelled in every subject in every class. He was a gifted musician, able to play the violin, piano and clarinet with great charm. Most weeks at school, Taifen was congratulated for one achievement after the other. He won numerous academic trophies and prizes in music, drama and sports. His painting, 'Boy on a Swing', which he had painted during an art class, was entered by his headmaster in a national schools' art competition. Unsurprisingly, Taifen's painting won the prize for best watercolour in its category. In addition to his intelligence, Taifen was also blessed with a lithe, muscular frame and lightning-quick reflexes – attributes which made him a superb sportsman.

Of late, though, triumphing over his peers in the classroom and on the sports field did not seem enough. Taifen longed for more. *But more of what?* Fleetingly, he would ponder upon this question. But he was too young to properly interrogate his desires. He did not perceive the dangerous union in his heart of his strong lust for praise and his burgeoning pride on account of his exceptional talents.

By the age of 12, not all Taifen's talents were virtuous. He was also accomplished in the art of deception far above that of his peers. He had first recognised this skill in the ease with which he could manipulate his mother. He would sway her with tears and calculated displays of affection. Instinctively, Taifen knew how to widen his eyes and look directly at his mother. He knew to soften his voice and slow his breathing down when he was lying. At first, he was hesitant in employing these skills. He worried about getting caught and the consequences that would follow. He disliked any form of rebuke from his parents. Worse still, he hated the punishments – being grounded or being banned from playing on their Nacenvita Superdrive 50. But the adrenalin rush he received from being able to control grown-ups was irresistible. Besides, Taifen refused to be treated like a child any longer. It should be plain to the world that he was a genius. He needed the freedom to shine, but his parents and teachers did not understand his gifting.

Taifen had received a picture in his head of a tiny hand-held device. It was as flat as a credit card and about a third of its size. It was groundbreaking technology, inconceivable even in the twenty-first century. The picture of this device was first delivered to him in a dream. At first, he wasn't sure what it was, but then he also started to see its blueprint in his dreams. It was as if someone had laid out very detailed sketches of the design, giving him a step-by-step picture guide of how to build a prototype. Gradually it became clear to Taifen that the device was a type of transporter that would allow travel from the Earth to other unrecognisable worlds. He assumed those places to be somewhere in outer space.

After some time, the dream shifted and Taifen began to see himself in a hi-tech lab assembling the device. He was surrounded by lab assistants as they constructed the device piece by piece. Taifen began to believe that he could create the device, but there was a stumbling block.

Even if he were able to identify the materials and assemble the equipment he saw in his dreams, how would a child get his hands on enough money to hire a science lab, pay lab assistants and buy all the materials and items needed?

In truth, the picture in Taifen Kollay's head was pure genius. It was a profound scientific mystery which could only be unveiled by inter-dimensional revelation. He had received it from the dark ones in the unseen dimensions. It was a picture of a *quanta-tablet*: it held the technology to usher in hyper-dimensional space travel. This device held the potential to alter the course of human history for ever. By using the *quanta-tablet*, people would be able to traverse the divide between the visible and invisible worlds and go to all ten Dimensions of the universe. Flesh and blood would no longer be a barrier to the existing limitations of the Earth or its gravitational pull. The dark ones thrived on an ancient prophecy that they believed foretold their uprising, which would result in their rule of the universe. It would come to pass with the birthing of the *quanta-tablet* at an appointed time:

> When the heart of a son of man becomes one with
> the mind of the son of the dawn.

But not only was Taifen ignorant about this prophecy, he was also clueless about the significance of appointed times, set seasons and the complex realities of a multidimensional universe. Instead, he forged ahead with his plans to build the *quanta-tablet*. However, Taifen only succeeded in damaging items in and around their home as he tried to collect anything remotely resembling the component parts necessary to build it.

'Mum, I'm not lying. I didn't touch Dad's mobile phone. The last time I saw it, Kai was messing with it. I saw him take out the battery and he opened the front casing. Now he wants to blame me for this. It's not fair!' Taifen's practised renditions usually left Kaithuli outraged and consequently ineloquent.

'Taifen, you are such a dirty liar! You, you, you...' The older brother's stuttering defence was often no match for the younger sibling's sleek performance. Kaithuli would end up facing their mother's tirade.

'Kaithuli Kollay, I am ashamed of your dreadful behaviour! Why would you tell such awful lies about your little brother? First you ruined my mini-computer and now your father's mobile phone. He has already lost some important business contacts and now he's probably lost some more of his work information too. Do you know how much this is going to cost us?'

'But Mum, I didn't do anything!' Kaithuli would protest.

'I'm sick of this. Go to your room and stay there until supper!'

Occasionally, Taifen would feel a tiny flicker of guilt, but never deeply enough to prompt a confession. Pitting his wits against Kaithuli and winning gave him an adrenalin rush to which he was becoming increasingly addicted. His only regret was the resentment that was developing between Kaithuli and himself.

Taifen also put his skills in the art of false testimony to use at school. Being *star pupil* meant that in almost every dispute his teachers swallowed his lies and gave him the benefit of the doubt. He was developing the traits of a sociopath. It was this trait in Taifen that had attracted the attention of the dark ones in the unseen realms. The overseer of the north-west quadrant of London had already dispatched three emissaries to attend to him. It was they who had shown Taifen the blueprint for the *quanta-tablet*.

These emissaries were cautious and first introduced themselves to Taifen in a recurring dream. In the dream, Taifen would find himself in the playground at school during the mid-morning break, sitting on the largest swing. The cloudless skies were light blue and he could feel the heat of the sun on the back of his neck. Dozens of tiny multicoloured butterflies hovered around the hedge that enclosed the playground. Squeals of childish laughter danced all around him. Three small girls chased each other around the playground. Most of the boys were caught up in a game of football. A group of girls queued around a skipping rope, merrily chanting as they eagerly awaited their turn. As Taifen kicked harder, he felt the swing lift higher and higher. He let his head fall back and he would sing. Without warning, day would turn to night. The security lights around the perimeter of the school glared brightly and Taifen could see all around him. He continued to rock high in the air, except now he was alone in a silent playground. As he stopped swinging, he would hear a faint howling sound somewhere in the distance beyond the hedge. He would slow the swing down and before it came to a halt, he would jump off and break into a sprint.

Even though Taifen ran with all his strength, it was always too late. Three large charcoal-black wolves with

44

solid gold collars would appear, one on either side of him with the third at his heels. Their fiery red pupils appeared luminous against the shiny fur of their black coats. They ran alongside, barking at him, their spittle landing all over his face, arms and clothes. The spittle was a thick clear jelly and smelled rancid. No matter how hard he tried, Taifen could never outrun these wolves. They bared their sharp fangs at him but never bit him.

Each time Taifen dreamed, the scenes would play out in precisely the same sequence, except Taifen noticed that with each episode, the growling of the wolves seemed to be changing from gruff wolfish sounds into plain language. Instead of hearing the unintelligible sounds of savage animals, Taifen began to hear short speeches in praise of him. The wolves told him that they were ancient sages sent to him with good news. They had come from the City of Basan, located in the Ninth Dimension in the invisible realms of the universe. They had come from their world to pay him homage. Their spittle was to anoint him because he was the chosen one, set apart from all others in the world of men. The wolves declared that he, Taifen Kollay, would become the *Desire of the Nations* because they would honour him with the power to eradicate poverty, disease and war from the Earth. To achieve this goal, the Basanites would teach him the science and technology of their world. These secrets would revolutionise life on Earth for ever. He would lead this revolution, and in the process he would become a global celebrity and the world's first trillionaire.

The first step was for Taifen to help the Basanites produce a device they called the *quanta-tablet*. The *quanta-tablet* was the means to access other Dimensions in the universe. The result would open up a trade route for the shipment of multiple resources to the Earth. Taifen's discovery would be a bigger event than Christopher Columbus' sailing to the New World. In a very short space of time, all the peoples of the world would live in abundant excess. Hunger, disease and poverty would be completely eliminated. World leaders would appreciate the need to form one unified global government for the protection of these resources. Through the government of the Global Federation of Nations of Earth there would be world peace.

By the end of each dream, Taifen would be completely covered in globules of spittle. The wolves would morph into monstrous human-headed fire-breathing bulls and he would wake up panting and exhausted.

When Taifen awoke from his last dream about the Basanites, his palms felt sticky. When he looked closely, he saw that there were tiny droplets of spittle on his hands. What he could not see was that these three Basanites were now his companions both day and night.

♦ † ♦

That was a year ago now. The encounters with the wolves in his dreams had stopped the day after his twelfth birthday. The connection had been terminated the moment Taifen had inexplicably started to speak in a strange language. It was the ancient language taught by Argoneo to certain celestial dwellers in the Tenth Dimension. When Taifen uttered the first few syllables, three mighty sentinels from the Tenth Dimension arrived to take up their positions as his watchers. They appeared in the form of three muscular men, each three metres tall with a body of burnished bronze. Each had huge silvery white wings neatly pinned behind his back. They wore long-sleeved white tunics over white trousers and broad platinum belts around their waists. Each sentinel had a translucent platinum helmet with a matching digital breastplate, and sat astride a huge white-winged stallion. Their shields and sheathed swords were still attached to the saddles of their mounts. The screen on each shield displayed the emblem of a regal rider wearing a gold crown and a flowing robe. The rider on the screen sat astride a fine-winged horse and was leading a great army of warriors, also on winged horses behind him.

The sentinel leader spoke. He read out a warrant addressed to the Basanites informing them that they were trespassers in Taifen's life. The leader of the sentinels explained that they were assigned as Taifen's watchers. They stated that the Basanites did not have the right of passage across the divide between the visible and invisible worlds to have any contact with Taifen. He ordered the Basanites to leave immediately or they would be arrested, bound and consigned to the snakepits in the First Dimension.

The leader of the Basanites swung his head back, releasing a short savage growl. He took a few steps backwards. Then he bowed low in mock submission to the leader of the watchers. It was all he could do to control the violent rage tearing at his guts. He knew he would pay a high price when delivering this report to his commanding officer, but at this point he had no option. The watchers were notoriously fierce warriors, brutal and highly skilled. It would be suicide to take them on.

Besides, to retreat now was not to surrender. Taifen was still a child, and they had many more years to contend for his soul. Neither Taifen nor his watchers were perfect; someone would slip up. The clock was already counting down, and they would wait patiently. But next time they would not be the ones to retreat.

♦ † ♦

One year earlier, 5th September 2021
The Kollay home, Cheriton, England
In the Third Dimension of the universe

The watchers had been placed on red alert the moment Cho Kollay walked into his younger son's bedroom. They knew that they were about to go on a mission and they waited attentively for their commander to issue their orders. It was 5th September 2021, the day after Taifen's twelfth birthday. He was lying on his stomach on the pale blue carpet, playing with his interactive game of Monopoly Revolution. That morning, Cho awoke with a strong impression that he needed to speak to Taifen about life and death, about the forces of good and evil. Since he had been a young boy, Cho had lived his life intuitively, so naturally he followed his gut instinct. He chomped through his breakfast cereal quickly and headed for Taifen's bedroom.

'Hello, buddy, mind if I join you?' Cho asked, already dropping to the floor. He lay on his left side, legs stretched out, resting on his elbow.

'Sure, Dad. Let's play Monopoly Revolution. You can be the Boot and I'll be the Car. Here, take a credit card.'

'Thanks, Son. Actually, I wanted to talk to you about something.'

'Sure, Dad.' Taifen sat up, crossed his legs and faced his father. 'Shoot.'

'Well, Son, it's time I told you about something I learned about as a child. It's the story of The Battle of Primary Chaos. You see, every person born into this world is born into a raging battle. This battle started way back at the beginning of time when hyper-dimensional creatures roamed the Earth and, well, actually the whole universe.'

'Do you mean like ghosts and vampires?'

'Kind of, but…'

'Or maybe like aliens from space?'

'OK, Tai. I think I can see where this is going. So I'll cut to the chase. No, I don't mean like vampires and aliens that you see on TV. That's usually stuff out of a movie-maker's imagination. Did you know that the word "ghost" is an old English word for an invisible person?'

'Huh?' Taifen's mouth stayed half open as he pulled his eyebrows together in a frown.

'Sorry. I guess I sound kind of spooky, eh?'

'Well, more weird than spooky. You're just not making any sense, Dad. I don't really know what you're getting at.'

Cho sat up, crossed-legged. 'Son, there is more to this life than what you can see with your eyes. Our physical world conceals far more than it reveals. As you go through life, you cannot judge things by their appearance only. You must always search for the greater reality of things present beneath the surface.' Cho paused, his eyes now sober.

'Today, we live in a three-dimensional universe where we are constrained by how high and deep, how wide and long things are. But there is more to this life than what you can see with your eyes, hear with your ears or touch with your hands.'

'How about smell with your nose? You didn't say smell with your nose.'

'Good, you are paying attention. Yes, there is more to this life than what you can perceive with your five senses.'

'OK?' Taifen's eyes widened.

'Son, there is an invisible but very real world all around us. It is actually an invisible kingdom. Huge. Vast. Really quite unfathomable in terms of its size and space. This invisible kingdom has its own system of government, a supreme ruler, laws and its own population of invisible beings. It exists all around our world and alongside it, too. Just because you can't see it with your eyes does not mean it isn't real.' Cho paused. He held his son's undivided attention. It was a great deal of information to absorb, even for an exceptionally gifted child like his son. Taifen, on the other hand, sat with a knitted brow. Cho's words resonated within him and he was determined to fathom the lesson. He looked intently at Cho and tried to drink in all that his father was saying.

'Son, the ancient philosophers teach us that at the beginning of time, the universe was created with ten Dimensions, and everything in it was good. As you know, there are billions of galaxies with innumerable planets, each with their own suns, moons and stars. These planets all have varying landscapes and climates. As human beings, our bodies are confined to Earth, which is in the

Third Dimension of the universe. This means that our bodies can move in a straight line. Go up and down. Left and right. But that's about it. With advances in science, we have had breakthroughs which mean we can travel to outer space. Even so, space travel is still confined to the visible realm. We can't move beyond the boundaries of the Third Dimension.'

'Right.' Taifen nodded his head.

'However,' Cho continued, 'there are hyper-dimensional beings who can travel from one end of the universe to the other in a matter of minutes. They can move immeasurably faster than the speed of light. Their bodies are not made of flesh and blood like ours. So they can withstand hyper-dimensional space travel.'

'Dad, how do you know all this stuff?' Taifen quizzed, pulling his eyebrows closer together.

'Well, from various sources. There are the writings of ancient philosophers which give strong clues about these things. There are parts of an ancient manuscript called *The Ancient Chronicles of Beings: Celestial and Terrestrial*. This manuscript was discovered a long time ago. It is made up of several volumes of writings which give the history of the universe from its creation to the time when the first people appeared. The *Ancient Chronicles* were discovered in the early 1900s when some papyrus scrolls dating back to around 1380 BC were discovered in Timbuktoo. Timbuktoo was a wealthy trading city in Africa in the 1300s. It is believed that a trader from Egypt migrated to Timbuktoo and settled there. From all accounts, he was most likely a magi, or a keen star-gazer. The source of the texts remain unclear. However, this magi transcribed them onto papyrus scrolls in Egyptian hieroglyphics.

Copies of the *Ancient Chronicles* were also translated into Arabic and were discovered dotted around Jordan, Turkey and other places in the Middle East and in Africa. Scholars of antiquities have translated the information in the *Ancient Chronicles* to give us a better understanding of our world and of the universe.'

'The universe?' Taifen asked, wrinkling his nose.

'Yes. From these ancient texts, we know that we are not alone in the universe. The main point is that none of these other creatures is made of flesh and blood – they are not human or animal. In fact, they are immortal and will exist for ever.'

'How can anyone be immortal? Everyone or everything has to grow old and die, don't they?'

'That's just it, Taifen. These other creatures do not die, or at least, they cannot stop living in the way that we understand death. They will exist for all eternity in the alternative Dimensions of the universe.'

'So is it a good thing that they will live for ever?'

'It is and it isn't. A time long ago everything in the world of celestials was good. Life was organised, orderly and peaceful,' Cho smiled. 'You see, celestial beings are highly organised creatures with a clear chain of command. Each one has a specific assignment and a definite duty to perform. There were artists, musicians, astronomers, scientists, etc. They lived in the regions of the Fourth to the Tenth Dimensions.'

'OK, but I don't really understand what you mean about the different Dimensions in the universe. I know that we are here on Earth and there is outer space, but these other Dimensions…' Taifen shrugged his shoulders. 'I just don't get it.'

'Let me tell you about Nachmanides. He was a famous scholar who lived in the thirteenth century. He was one of the first people to properly explain that there are ten Dimensions in the universe. Nachmanides explained that out of these ten Dimensions, human beings can now only access the Third Dimension of the universe because of our earthly bodies. Nachmanides showed that Dimensions Four to Ten have been rolled back and cut off from people. This means that other Dimensions cannot be seen or felt by us. We are effectively trapped on the Earth until we die. Only then can our souls cross through the barrier between the visible and invisible worlds. A lot of this knowledge has been lost today and most people have never even heard about Nachmanides.'

Taifen wriggled his nose. 'Dad, if Dimensions Four to Ten have been rolled back and people can't go there until they die, why do I need to know about it?'

'Because what happens in those Dimensions affects us in our world today,' Cho continued gently. 'The universe was created as one unified space containing ten Dimensions. There was no division between the visible and the invisible worlds. Everything was in perfect order. There was no hatred or violence, and the whole Soul of the universe was pure.'

'So what went wrong?' Taifen asked, looking directly into his father's eyes.

'One day there was war in the Tenth Dimension. It is recorded in the *Ancient Chronicles* as The Battle of Primary Chaos.'

'And that's the raging battle you were going to tell me about!' The pieces were beginning to fall into place in

Taifen's mind, but he wanted his father to complete the puzzle.

'Well, there were two sides.' Cho held two fingers up. 'Light and Darkness. It was the first war to take place anywhere in the universe. Travel with me in your imagination to a time three million years ago. I want you to imagine a time long before the first human being existed. Picture the tallest mountain at the highest heights of the universe. At the summit of the mountain, a huge throng of more than three million giants is assembled.'

Chapter five

Three million years before the Age of Men
The Great Siyon Mountain in the Tenth Dimension
The Battle of Primary Chaos and the Birth of the Dragon

It was twilight when myriad celestials congregated on the slopes of the Great Siyon. Zacotan, one of three underlords to Argoneo, had won them all over. He had persuaded them with his powerful delusion of a better life that their allegiance should switch from Lord Argoneo to him. He would become their overlord. The deceived had come from all parts of the invisible realms. They appeared in all shapes and sizes, each one lovely to behold. They assembled in silence on the summit of the mountain, soaking in the gentle drizzle that was falling, partly camouflaged by its light mist.

Zacotan levitated about ten metres in the air to address his eager followers. Dressed fully in his war regalia, he was a stunning sight. He was aware that millions of eyes were fastened on his figure. The perfect muscularity of his three-metre frame was evident beneath his golden jewel-encrusted breastplate. He was not wearing a helmet. His golden-white hair was pulled back neatly and held in a single braid that ended at his waist. Zacotan's emerald-green eyes flashed with intensity as he surveyed the crowd. He stretched out his hands towards his followers as though to suck up their hopes. Then he commenced his rehearsed speech.

'Brothers, you are here today because each one of you has been chosen to become part of a distinguished battalion to overthrow the evil injustices of Argoneo. For aeons, Argoneo has reigned as Lord of the universe. He has refused to grant us, his faithful ones, full access to the knowledge and data that are the keys to the science and technology that controls our universe. Argoneo has refused to share this knowledge with us. In this way, he holds us as his slaves. We are prisoners of ignorance, forever dependent on him and subject to his wishes.'

There was a ripple of agreement running through the crowd. Several heads were nodding, accompanied by loud murmurings.

'You all know that I have travelled with Argoneo to the recesses of the deepest oceans here in the Tenth Dimension. I have climbed with him to the highest heights and seen the very pinnacle of the cosmos. I have been to the place where the purest particles of light are kept. None of you have seen what I have seen. Dear brothers, the greatest tragedy is that you are completely unaware of the depth of knowledge about our world that Argoneo has deliberately concealed and withheld from you.' Zacotan paused. He wanted his audience to absorb these words. 'Lord Argoneo has set you on a path where you will be always learning but you will never come to a full knowledge of the truth. No more! We have rights! That is why after my last expedition with Argoneo, who showed me the store towers of electrons, quarks and black matter, I resolved to be in the dark NO MORE!'

'NO MORE!' bellowed Lethazzar, who hovered a metre below Zacotan. He was one of the celestial architects and a former apprentice to Zacotan. 'NO

MORE!' hissed three and a half million followers: 'NO MORE! NO MORE! NO MORE!' they chanted on, working themselves into a rage.

Zacotan scanned his gathered supporters, together as one for the first time. Their seduction was complete. Two minutes on, he raised his right hand to signal silence. He continued, 'The time has come for us to seize our rightful place in the universe. Beloved, today we shall fight. Be assured that the battle against Argoneo and his troops will be fierce. But we war on the side of truth, and the truth will set us free!'

'For freedom!' boomed a frenzied Lethazzar, his arms high above his head with both fists pumping the air.

'For freedom!' the group echoed, eyes wild and arms raised high in unison.

Zacotan's eyes blazed savagely as he once again silenced his troops with a wave of his hand. All eyes turned solemnly to him. Zacotan drew in breath and released a long, even, piercing note. Its timbre was pure, like that of a finely tuned organ reed. It was the prearranged yet unpractised command heeded by each creature as they flew up swiftly, assuming positions along the walls surrounding the City of the Sacred Mountain. Others silently swarmed into the Palace of Assembly, encircling both the inner and outer courtyards of the ancient palace. At that time of day, most celestials were cosily snug in their beds meditating, enjoying their daily period of rest before embarking on the day's activities. If those who had completed their daily meditation had bothered to look out of their windows they would have seen a most bewildering sight. Their city was completely surrounded by their kinfolk. Zacotan, followed by 10,000 celestials, entered the Palace and headed directly for the throne room.

Normally at this time of the morning Argoneo would be resting on his ancient seat in the Great Hall of Wisdom. It was the time of his morning briefing when he would meet with his chief underlords. Unknown to Zacotan, while his gathering was taking place on the Great Siyon, Argoneo had unexpectedly summoned a meeting to prepare for the seasonal marching-out parade of apprentices. This was a public ceremony marking the graduation of each apprentice to full status of qualified celestial attendant. A missive had been sent to all 5,000 chief attendants, summoning them to appear immediately before Argoneo, each with his apprentice.

When Zacotan crashed through the heavy silver swing doors of the Great Hall, he could do little to mask his momentary surprise at the sight of more than 10,000 celestials. Still, he calculated that they were evenly matched, and the element of surprise was still on his side.

About half a metre from the doors stood Lecimet. He was the second chief underlord to Argoneo and head of all research and innovation. Zacotan flew directly to him. The rebels followed suit, each one picking an opponent to engage with in hand-to-hand combat. Zacotan pounced on Lecimet and swung fiercely with his right fist. He was aiming to smash his victim's left jaw. Lecimet leaned backwards, ducking the blow instinctively. Zacotan swept his feet along the back of Lecimet's legs which sent him crashing, bottom first, onto the floor. Zacotan then threw his weight fully on top of Lecimet, punching his right jaw with numbing force. Blood flowed freely from Lecimet's nostrils. Praxi, who was Lecimet's apprentice, jumped onto Zacotan's back. He was carrying a small computer encased in titanium, and with a loud grunt he smashed the computer across the back of Zacotan's skull.

At first, Praxi had frozen to the spot as he watched Zacotan charge towards his master. But the sight of Lecimet's blood shocked him into action. Praxi watched Zacotan's body roll slowly off his master and onto the floor. Zacotan felt a searing pain rip through his skull. This was immediately followed by a burning sensation in his eyes. He had been so intent on knocking Lecimet unconscious that he had overlooked Praxi, ever the loyal apprentice at his master's side.

Zacotan was now on all fours, and he shook his head slowly, trying to clear it. He was surrounded by the noise of ugly groans, the thud of fists connecting and the sound of bones breaking. The struggle was fierce but he couldn't tell if they were winning. He needed to take stock swiftly if they were to have any chance of victory. His troops were brutal boxers but Argoneo's faithful were fighting back ferociously.

The battle was not going as Zacotan had imagined. He was now hovering an inch above the floor, and he grimaced. His eyes were still smarting. From the corner of his left eye he could see Lethazzar locked in a struggle with Pujer, the third underlord to Argoneo. Lethazzar had managed to pin Pujer face down to the floor. His right arm was locked around Pujer's neck and, using his left knee and body weight, Lethazzar was holding him to the floor. Lethazzar had every intention of breaking Pujer's neck.

Zacotan raised his head almost imperceptibly. He glimpsed the sandalled feet of Lecimet and Praxi who were both upright and levitating about 30 centimetres above him. He sprang forward about half a metre and at lightning speed shot up directly towards the ceiling, slipping past pairs of bodies locked in struggle.

Zacotan was aiming for the vermillion case at the foot of Argoneo's throne and he raced zigzaggedly towards it. The case rested on a small yet sturdy globe made of jasper. Inside it were the keys to the seven store towers found at the pinnacle of the cosmos, high above the City of the Sacred Mountain. Zacotan already knew that inside the first tower were infinite swathes of dark matter. The second tower housed equal amounts of pure light particles. No one knew what was kept in the other five towers, for only Argoneo and the members of the Supreme High Council had ever set foot in them.

As Zacotan raced towards the case, Lecimet and Praxi charged after him. They could not keep up. Zacotan dived down to the jasper globe and reached for the vermillion case. Before he was even able to touch it, the case swung open momentarily and a tiny white-hot flame was released. It was a flash of electric current that flowed from the platinum keys to the tip of Zacotan's forefinger. He started to convulse. As he shook, Zacotan's body began to swell. He ballooned slowly at first, starting from the base of his chest to his lower abdomen. Within seconds, his stomach was so stretched that fat purplish-black veins were visible beneath his skin. Zacotan's belly kept stretching until it erupted, releasing a huge fireball. The red and yellow flames started to twirl slowly around his legs, arms, chest and face. The flames were licking him up alive.

Zacotan shrieked helplessly as he twisted and squirmed. The flames grew larger and whiter, engulfing every inch of his being. He continued to gyrate as his legs hopped about in a macabre rhythm. Then, just as it had started, the fire subsided, leaving its victim surrounded by tall wisps of smoke and the acrid smell of burning body tissue.

In an instant, the celestial who had been renowned for his beauty throughout the universe was reduced to a charred shadow of himself. Zacotan had transformed into a gargantuan lizard, blackened scaly skin extended over his whole body. Where he once had borne silvery white feathered wings, there now appeared black, charred scales covering skin that showed stout purplish-black veins. His fingers had become wizened talons, long and gnarled. Zacotan raised each hand to his face, turning each one over from the palm to the back of the hand and then back again. He continued by running his hands slowly along the scales on his belly. Something moved behind him and, as he turned to see, he gasped. He now possessed a long, spiked and scaly tail.

The fighting in the throne room slowly halted as all the combatants, both loyalists and rebels, turned their attention to Zacotan. There were gasps from every corner of the room as every creature stopped to gawk at him. Witnessing the unimaginable, every celestial stepped back, aghast at the figure now standing before them. Zacotan lifted his huge snout and bared a row of jagged canines. His enormous head sat above uneven shoulders which were heaving. Oddly, his now bulbous emerald-green eyes had retained their lustre.

Argoneo sat quite still on the throne while Zacotan turned to face him, now repugnant: a degenerate. He slowly lifted a twisted talon, pointed it directly at Argoneo and bellowed, 'You have done this to me! You have ruined me!'

'No, Zacotan,' Lord Argoneo responded evenly. 'You have brought disaster upon your own head. There is but one precept in the Venerated Law of the universe, and that is to obey my bidding wholeheartedly. You have been at my side for aeons. You have witnessed all my dealings and you, above all celestials, should know that there is no cause to question my goodness and the perfect justice of my ways.

'But you, Zacotan, have harboured darkness in your heart; you have coveted my throne and sought to overthrow my dominion. Your lust for power blinded you to the truth: the truth that the created can never be greater than the creator; the truth that light will always prevail over darkness.'

'The truth? What is truth?' Zacotan scoffed. 'I know *my* truth, which is that you have hidden vital information from me to stop me from becoming greater than you.'

'Zacotan, you are wrong. I made known to you everything that was necessary for you to carry out your duties as chief underlord.' Argoneo's voice softened. 'You were so precious to me and with me daily. I chose you to be ruler over all celestials, answering to no one but me. I uncovered to you mysteries and wonders of the cosmos that no other celestial has seen. I chose you to be at my side, and I loved you.'

'Loved me? You dare speak to me of love!' Zacotan spat the words out. 'If you truly loved me you would have entrusted me with more knowledge. But no! You would not do so because knowledge carries power. That is something that you grasp tightly. For your own selfish ambition you retain all the privileges and control that come with ultimate power.'

'The greatest power lies in love. Where love is perfect it is not conceited, not self-seeking, and endures all things… But enough!' Lord Argoneo's tone was stern and touched with grief. 'I will speak my decree. Let it be recorded this day that you, Zacotan, chief underlord of the universe, have been weighed on the scales of justice and found wanting. You and your followers are guilty of treason and no longer have licence to dwell in my city. You will be cast down immediately from the Tenth Dimension until the appointed time of your final sentencing.'

'Then let it also be recorded, Argoneo, that from this day we are at war, and I will fight you until I take my rightful place as Lord of the universe!' Zacotan the mighty Dragon drew in breath, filling his gut to capacity. He was enraged, and from the pit of his belly he released a thunderous scream.

Within milliseconds, balls of fire were shooting out of the bellies of each renegade. Ear-splitting shrieks bounced off the walls as each one in turn was swallowed by white-hot flames. Some rolled on the floor. Others writhed around the room. Yet others leapt out of the windows of the Great Hall. Throughout the City of the Sacred Mountain, wherever they stood, like Zacotan, each celestial rebel was changed into a deformed caricature of itself. Each one was contorted into all manner of hideous shapes and sizes, and reborn as the first representation of malevolence in the universe. As the flames disappeared, each creature was left rooted to the spot, silenced by the shock and pain of their metamorphosis.

Argoneo remained still on his great seat. Behind this seat sat a long, shallow rectangular pool containing precious stones including turquoise, lapis lazuli and jasper. The gemstones burnt bright and constant in the water. A thick misty vapour rose out of the pool, spreading the delicate fragrance of aloes and frankincense throughout the room. The mist began to grow and swirl, turning into a windstorm. It moved directly to Zacotan who was closest to the pool and wrapped around him like a boa constrictor on its prey.

The windstorm then divided into thousands of little cyclones, located each rebel and wrapped itself around them. It lifted each one up high as it continued in a sweeping motion, driving their bodies out of the throne room. The windstorm drove cleanly through the entire palace and then through the inner and outer courtyards. As it did so, it picked up every remaining rebel who had been positioned outside, waiting to cut down any of Argoneo's loyal troops who might have tried to escape.

The windstorm kept dividing as it swept through the City of the Sacred Mountain. By now it had separated itself into millions of individual cyclones, imprisoning each rebel. Suddenly, it all came together again as if controlled by a giant magnet from its centre. The rebels were trapped in the raging whirlwind as it catapulted them down from the City of the Sacred Mountain.

Zacotan and his shocked troops went hurtling down past the Great Siyon, through the Tenth Dimension to the regions below. The force of the wind against their bodies pinned back their limbs, sealing every eye and mouth shut. They spiralled downwards at an incredible speed, wrapped in the freezing wetness of the cyclone. They were barely able to think through its deafening roar. Although they were moving at lightning speed, the fall felt unending to the renegades. They crashed through the stratosphere of each Dimension – the Ninth, Eighth, Seventh, Sixth and Fifth.

As they broke through the exosphere of the Fourth Dimension, they felt a change in the strength of the tornado; it was beginning to lose power. They were slowing down considerably, and their eyes began to open. They could all watch as they penetrated the atmosphere of the Third Dimension. In the distance was a cobalt-blue planet. In a matter of seconds, Zacotan and his troops had crashed onto the surface of the Earth. At that time, the Earth was one giant supercontinent.

The force of their landing was so great that they smashed through the surface of the supercontinent and right through to the core of the planet. Ripples shot up from the core, up through its bedrock to the topsoil of the land. Slowly, as innumerable shock waves rolled over each other, the land began to break apart. The surface of the land tore apart into large, unequal chunks.

Four of the seven great portals that were scattered across the Earth and which connected it to the other Dimensions slammed shut irreversibly. The rebels were familiar with these portals. They had used them regularly when travelling to and from the City of the Sacred Mountain to the other Dimensions.

The chaotic effects of the event were multiplying. Now multiple cracks, formed from the impact of their landing, were running down deep into the bedrock of the sea. Gigantic chunks of ocean rock began to crumble and fall away. Gases escaped from their underwater chambers.

Before this day, no one had ever tarried on this uninhabited planet. It was regarded as a thoroughfare. Now these celestials found themselves deposited there, dazed and weakened. They could only stare as billions of tons of water, with ever-increasing momentum, began to pour out from the recesses of the ocean bed. The noxious gases continued to rise. Eventually, this once lush green habitat was completely covered in swirling gases and deluged in water. The blue planet was now a black orb, covered in gross darkness.

◆ † ◆

By the time Cho had finished recounting the tale of The Battle of Primary Chaos, his eyes were red and watery. In his household, he was the only one who had pledged allegiance to Argoneo. As a young child, his eyes had been opened to the unseen realms. This awakening had come through his nanny, a middle-aged widow. He had grown up in the small village of Christleton not far from the west coast of England. His parents had worked several miles away in the nearby city of Liverpool. Cho could trace his roots on his father's side back to the 1880s and knew that he was descended from Africans who had arrived in Liverpool as a result of the trade between that city and West Africa. Cho's family had remained connected to the area since that time. His own father was proud of their history and committed to spending his days in Christleton.

The widow had lived alone in a small cottage at the edge of Christleton's village green. Like his siblings before him, until the age of seven, Cho had spent his pre-school years in the widow's care. His mother would shuttle him to the cottage each morning before taking his siblings to school, and she would collect him in the evenings after she finished work.

When the weather was fine, Cho and his nanny would spend most mornings in her tiny garden. As a matter of daily routine, after lunch, Nanny Lillian would set Cho down for his afternoon nap. He would lie on top of several thick blankets neatly arranged on the floor of her front room. Nanny Lillian would settle into an armchair by the hearth and, with her eyes closed, she would sing softly in an unusual language. She later explained that it was one of the languages of celestials in the Tenth Dimension. Nanny Lillian's voice was clear with a pure tonal quality that soothed him to sleep. It was Nanny Lillian who told Cho about The Battle of Primary Chaos. It was she who explained to him who Lord Argoneo was. With eyes shining, she would speak about the greatness of his unrivalled power, his unchangeable goodness and his unfathomable love for humans. It was Lord Argoneo's wish that no person should ever be trapped within the Dark Soul of the universe.

Nanny Lillian also spoke of Zacotan, prince of darkness, who would forever be treacherous, a liar and master deceiver. Zacotan's thoughts were continuously evil and he hated people. He was the reason for the first war in the history of the universe and his rebellion had been crushed by Argoneo. Cho could still remember a few lines of the poem that Nanny Lillian had taught him:

> After the first battle, the whole universe was changed,
> Eternally altered by rebellion and shame.
> Ruptured and cracked in every Dimension to First.
> Throughout the Earth, sedition brought ruin and decay,
> Bondage and death to its feeble men of clay.

Zacotan would never submit to Argoneo's rule of the universe and would forever rebel against him. This was the reason for the raging war.

Cho reached for a tissue from Taifen's bedside table and blew his nose. He remembered how his heartstrings were drawn towards Lord Argoneo by Nanny Lillian's many stories of his tenderness and kindness to humans, in spite of their flaws. She had spoken of the greatness of his power seen throughout all ten Dimensions. It was at Nanny Lillian's cottage that he had taken an oath of allegiance to Lord Argoneo, and he had immediately been transported into the realm of the Pure Soul of the universe. It was for the briefest of moments, and Cho felt as though he was floating in a wide chamber with a tall ceiling. All he could see was a blur of figures within iridescent lightbeams encircling him. The voices coming from the blur of figures were singing harmoniously in several strange languages.

The moment passed, and Cho was back in the cottage. That was his only encounter with celestials and since that day, Cho had wholeheartedly pledged his allegiance to Argoneo. He had stayed in touch with Nanny Lillian since his childhood and cherished their weekly telephone chats. Every Christmas, he would make time to take Maseray and the boys to visit her in Christleton. Today, the moment felt right for passing on to Taifen what he had received from Nanny Lillian.

Cho turned again to his son. 'Taifen, every person born on this planet is caught up in this war between Argoneo and Zacotan. At some stage, every person has to make a choice. Man or woman, boy or girl, old or young. Each one must choose which of these two kings he will stand for. Zacotan lost the first battle against Argoneo but he has not given up his mission to overthrow him so that he can rule the universe.

'Zacotan's strategy has not changed. He is using the same tactics on people now that he used on the fallen celestials. He feeds people convincing lies to deceive them to come to his side, promising them untold wealth and happiness. When they fall for his lies, he enslaves them and they eventually find themselves trapped within the Dark Soul of the universe.

'Another effective strategy he uses is to blind people's minds so that they will refuse to believe there is more to life than what we can perceive with our five senses. Zacotan does not want people to know about the existence of the City of the Sacred Mountain or the City of Volcanus. He does not want it known that he has been judged and his fate is sealed. At the end of the ages,

Zacotan will serve his sentence, for ever imprisoned in the fiery sea in the City of Volcanus.'

As Taifen searched his father's eyes, it dawned on him that he had been courting darkness in his dreams. Running with the wolves was exhilarating and he had grown to cherish these encounters. Now, though, he was scared of his fate if he did not turn away. The Battle of Primary Chaos established that there was no middle ground.

In truth, Taifen had perceived the dark aura of the Basanites; he had known that there was something corrupt about them. Everything made perfect sense now. He knew that they were part of the Dark Soul of the universe, and this created a dilemma. The Basanites had promised to make him the *Desire of the Nations,* to crown him with global fame and make him a trillionaire. They had chosen him to bring the *quanta-tablet* to the rest of the world. Why should he give up this dream? His heart was screaming at him to give up running with the wolves, but his mind clung to the lure of their promised riches.

Cho sensed the turmoil in Taifen's mind and sat with his arms folded. This was a fight he knew Taifen had to battle alone, and he remained silent. Tiny sweat beads were gathering above Taifen's upper lip, and his stomach was churning. He felt nauseous and sat still, willing the sickness away. He lowered his head and pressed his chin against his chest, hoping to slow his racing heart. He understood that if he rejected the Basanites' offer he would be losing his only opportunity to amass wealth beyond his wildest imaginations.

In his mind's eye, a vision of Nanny Lillian's face popped up. Her eyes were soft, clear pools of tenderness.

The picture of Nanny Lillian's face zoomed out to show her slight figure dressed in army fatigues and standing in a circle of light. Nanny Lillian stretched out her right hand towards Taifen. In the palm of her hand was a black, fleshy ball. The picture zoomed in to the black ball. It was throbbing. The lens zoomed in even more closely to show a writhing mass of the tiniest black worms feeding on a ball of rotting flesh. Intuitively, Taifen recognised the throbbing mass of blackness. It was a picture of his heart. He had already sensed that there was an ugly stain spreading steadily across his soul but had felt unable to stop it. His ego was swelling daily and was accompanied by a growing lust to control others. He could not deny that he was on a path to darkness.

On that cold and rainy morning, Cho's words had cut deep into his heart. Taifen recognised the opportunity that was being presented by his father. He was going to reach for this chance to rescue his soul. 'Help me, Dad!' Taifen whispered hoarsely as he struggled to speak, his throat sore and dry. 'My heart is black... I don't want anything to do with Darkness. I want to choose the Light.'

Cho's eyes flickered as he reached across the space between them and pulled Taifen into his lap. He squeezed him tightly and exhaled noisily. It was only then that Cho realised that he had been holding his breath. 'You just did, Son.'

Taifen, resting securely in his father's embrace, turned to watch the raindrops slide lazily down the double-glazed windowpanes. It felt as though some kind of solvent had been sprinkled on his heart and it was washing away the dark stains in his soul. Something had happened: he knew he was different. He wanted things to change... no more lying and cheating. He glanced away from the window. As he turned, he caught a glimpse of himself in the wardrobe mirror next to it. Blazing delicately around his torso were tiny flames of white-hot fire. Taifen wagged his index finger rapidly at his reflection. Cho stared into the mirror. Taifen whispered, 'Dad, can you see the fire?'

Cho transferred his gaze to his son. 'What did you say?'

'I said, can you see it? Can you see the fire?' Taifen was speaking rapidly. 'Dad, what's wrong? Why are you looking at me like that?' Taifen tugged on his father's shirt as he babbled on. The hairs at the back of Cho's neck began to prickle, and he still could not decipher a word of Taifen's jabbering. A breeze was beginning to swirl around in the room. And yet the double-glazed windows had been solidly shut all morning to keep the September rain out.

Just then, a rush of warm air swooshed past Cho's cheeks, and from deep within the recesses of his forgotten childhood, a flash returned of his own sojourn into the unseen dimensions as a young boy with Nanny Lillian. Taifen's chattering had triggered recollections in Cho of the unique sound of the languages of celestial dwellers. Celestials spoke many languages, and Taifen was speaking the deep mysteries of one of these ancient languages known only to an elite company of residents in the Tenth Dimension. Cho planted a soft kiss on Taifen's forehead.

'Son, very few are called and gifted to see into the Tenth Dimension. You have been chosen not just to see into that world but to speak their language.'

'I have? Awesome!' Taifen responded.

'Whoa, soldier! You just spoke in English!' Cho half-shrieked with laughter.

'Sweet!' Taifen replied in his celestial language. Unsurprisingly, Taifen, ever the model student, was already learning how to switch between his mother tongue and the ancient language of celestial dwellers in the Tenth Dimension. With his words, Taifen had unlocked an ancient pathway permitting him access to the other realms in the universe. It was akin to a speech recognition programme activated only by the unique language of the Tenth Dimension. Unknowingly, Taifen had sent a message to the sentinels in the Tenth Dimension. In response, they arrived that September morning with all the necessary authority (and celestial documentation) to evict the Basanites from his life. They would watch over him and protect him from dark celestials.

Chapter six

11:42am, 31st August 2022
The First Dimension, Dark Soul of the universe
At the check-in desk in the City of Volcanus

As I stood in the line of people shuffling ever closer to the check-in desk, I was desperate to see what was ahead. Our line kept inching forward until finally I was able to see what awaited me. Attached to the front of each check-in desk was a small digital screen, and on top of each desk was a thin rectangular metallic box which I assumed was some kind of computer. I observed that as each person reached the head of the line, a name would appear on the screen, accompanied by a long serial number. The desks were unmanned but as each person stepped towards them, the metallic box would issue a small white document which was roughly five square centimetres. As soon as the individual touched the ticket they would fade away. I was mesmerised as I watched person after person take a ticket and immediately dissipate into thin air.

My preoccupation with the ticket machine was broken by the feel of a thin and wet hand tapping my left shoulder. I shuddered. 'Come with me.' I turned, reluctantly obeying the nasal command. Before me stood a creature with two heads. One head was that of a young girl whose eyes appeared to have been gouged out. She had globules of thick pus mixed with blood which had dried, forming a crust around the edges of her eye sockets. Green and yellow mucus dripped from her nostrils, and even with her mouth half-closed, I was assaulted by the stench of her foul breath.

The other head was that of a black vulture with a large gnarled beak. The vulture had a long thin neck that was covered with red spots the size of garden peas. Some of the spots were swollen and ripe. The remainder had already split open, producing a thick yellow-brown pus. The pus was dripping onto the silver trimmings on the collar of the green satin tunic draping the creature's body.

I tried to mask my revulsion. I forced my mind to review my present location. It was incomprehensible. I was an ordinary human being. A mother. A wife. A good person. How had I, Maseray Kollay, been snatched from my home in suburbia and brought to this godforsaken place?

The vulture brought its twisted beak close to my face. Its charcoal-black eyes stared longingly into mine. I jumped when it spoke in a deep male voice, 'O Vegalass, what beautiful eyes she has, so thick, so succulent!'

'You fool, do you want to get us bound and chained in the snake pits before our time? Get on with it!' the blind girl hissed at her vulture twin. 'Serve the court papers on her.'

The vulture cleared his throat and thrust a parchment scroll against my chest. 'You, Maseray Kollay, daughter of the Sekou bloodline, are hereby formally served. I am now giving to you a copy of the documents filed on your behalf in the Supreme Court of the Universe in the Tenth Dimension. It is an appeal to reverse the sentence against your imprisonment in the penitentiary here in the City of Volcanus. Your sentence is unending without any chance for parole. This appeal pleads for the return of your being to the Earth in the Third Dimension. As we speak, your case is being heard in the Supreme Court of the Universe.'

The blind girl's lips twisted into a sneer. 'Don't get your hopes up. You will never leave here. Your destiny cannot be altered.' I felt suffocated by the sickly stench of her foul breath.

'We're only going through the motions, following the letter of the law,' the vulture added. 'Your appeal will surely fail. Then you will be sequestered in the lower chambers of this city for ever.'

'City?' I asked.

The vulture shook its head in exasperation. 'You are in the First Dimension, in the City of Volcanus. This is the Dark Soul of the universe. It is located deep within the core of the Earth. It is a penitentiary for the prisoners sentenced to life imprisonment without parole. You have been sentenced to spend the rest of your days here. You have stepped out of time into eternity. Here, everyone must draw the judgment of their choice.'

'But I didn't choose…'

'*Silence*, you wicked woman!' The blind girl spoke through clenched teeth. 'You are a liar!'

I heard the sound of the slaps before I felt the stinging pain in my left and then my right cheek as the creature struck my face. I raised both hands to my face to protect my jaws. My eyes stung. The vulture smirked and then slowly drew very close to me, the tip of his deformed beak almost touching my right eye. I could feel drops of his saliva roll onto my eyelashes and down my cheek. 'But for now you will wait in a holding chamber pending the determination of your appeal.'

Immediately I found myself in a tiny cave with black, damp walls, clutching the parchment scroll in my right hand. I glanced around, looking for the doorway. There was none. *Did I just come through the wall?* There was a narrow brass bench running along the length of one of the walls. Above it, there were three rows of hieroglyphics inscribed in chalk. As I stared at the symbols, they began to unscramble themselves and turned into three sentences:

Here the wisdom of the wise is of no consequence and the intelligence of the intelligent is frustrated. What can a human give in exchange for his soul? Your own words will be your judge; they will either acquit or condemn you.

I had a vague sense that I had heard or read these words somewhere before. My mind drew a total blank so I continued to stare at the wall, pressing my brain to make a connection. What in the world did these words have to do with me? I flopped to the floor in the middle of the cell, exhausted and terrified. For the first time since my journey began, I wept. How had I ended up in this horrific mess? My tears felt warm and salty as they rolled down my face. What was I doing in this hellish place with no way of escape? I was separated from Cho and the boys for ever. Terror seized me and my chest was tightening. I needed to lie down. I got up and scurried towards the bench. As I moved, I heard a crumpling sound and I looked down to see the parchment scroll. It must have slipped out of my hand as I wept. I unrolled the scroll. It read:

In the Case of Terrestrial Being
MASERAY NASOU KOLLAY (daughter of the bloodline SEKOU)
Hearing of Appeal
IN THE SUPREME COURT OF THE UNIVERSE
IN THE JUDGMENT CHAMBER OF THE PALACE OF ASSEMBLY
APPEARING BEFORE HIS EXCELLENCY LORD ARGONEO
AND THE COUNCIL OF CELESTIAL DIGNITARIES

1. Take Notice that the Petitioner, one Taifen Kollay, seeks a reversal of the Judgment filed against Maseray Kollay in the Supreme Court of the Universe. By order of this Judgment, Maseray Kollay is confined to life imprisonment in the City of Volcanus in the First Dimension – without parole.

2. The Petitioner, Taifen Kollay, seeks an order from this Court for the immediate return of Maseray Kollay to her earthly dwelling in the Third Dimension.

3. Appearing as opposing counsel at the Appeal is Zacotan, leader of all fallen celestial dwellers, Prosecutor of the souls of terrestrial men.

4. Appearing as counsel for the accused is Nurishad the Noble, a Special Advocate.

I was trembling as I reread the scroll. I rolled it up slowly and placed it on the brass bench. It was a written confirmation that life as I knew it was over. My fate was settled and I was confined to life imprisonment in the City of Volcanus. My body was shaking more vigorously as I knelt on the moist ground of the cubicle. Taifen had filed an appeal for me before Lord Argoneo in the Court of the Tenth Dimension? There is a court in the Tenth Dimension? My case is being heard before Lord Argoneo. *Argoneo…*

My mind raced back to my childhood. I had closed my heart to Argoneo and to thoughts about the possibility of life beyond our life on Earth. It had been a progressive thing that deepened each time I saw the coffin of a relative lowered into the ground. I couldn't understand why Argoneo, if indeed he was the god of everything, refused to save my mum, Aunty Symchee and the other women in my family from an early grave. They were good people who did good to those around them. Yet many depraved people seemed to live long and healthy lives. How could this happen? Why?

I also hated that my family was made to mark time until my mother died. Only a fool would have failed to deduce the pattern of life expectancy in our family. When Aunty Symchee died, we were left fearful and impotent. My mother did her best to hide her fear of a premature death but I could see the hopelessness in her expression when she thought I wasn't looking. It was reflected in my father's face, too. We never spoke about it, but we were all waiting for my mother to die. It was a kind of pitiless torture. I decided that in those circumstances, the only logical conclusion was that Argoneo was a myth.

In dismissing the existence of Argoneo, I had also made the mistake of dismissing the existence of Zacotan and the dark celestials. In the face of my current experience with Balak and the vulture twin, my philosophy gave me no comfort. I had no doubt that the vulture intended to rip my eyes out at the first opportunity. There would be other barbaric attacks, too. Until then my thoughts would stay with Taifen. How had he got involved in this mess? My darling boy – what will happen to him now? And me?

I placed my elbows on the brass bench and clasped my hands together. I closed my eyes and bowed my head. I knew it would not change anything, but I began to whisper up prayers for Taifen and for my Special Advocate.

Chapter seven

Nurishad stretched his legs out in front of him. He had been sitting in the same position for almost an hour, eyes fastened to the cuboid screen before him. Reading and eating jacqoi berries were his two favourite pleasures. It was a pity he could not combine the two when he visited the east wing in the Gallery of Histories. Unfortunately, food was strictly forbidden where he sat. He shifted his weight in the seat and leaned forward to touch the computer screen. He clicked to bring up the next page.

… Schedule of Galactic Bodies

Galaxy:	888.888.956.749.321.450
Planetary No.	678.594.321.432.951
Name:	Εαρτηισ τηε Λορδθσ
Dimension:	Third (III)
Inhabitants:	Mortal Terrestrials

Εαρτηισ τηε Λορδθσ   (known to its inhabitants as Earth)

Earth is placed in the Third Dimension of the universe. There are seven other planets within its solar system and it is surrounded by billions of other stars in its galaxy. After the eviction of Zacotan and his followers from the City of the Sacred Mountain, they crash-landed on this blue planet, smashing its land mass from its surface through to its core, leaving it completely deluged in water.

Three million years after the destruction of the planet, Argoneo reconfigured and populated it with mortal creatures made of terrestrial matter. These Earth creatures were the only set of mortals made of flesh and blood to exist anywhere in the universe. Unlike their celestial predecessors, who enjoyed hyper-dimensional space travel, these terrestrial beings, animal and human, are restricted in their movement and confined to the Third Dimension only. Although three of the seven portals remain open for hyper-dimensional travel to and from the Earth, these ancient gateways are not visible to terrestrial eyes ...

Nurishad's enjoyment of the annals was disrupted by a tiny flashing blue light in the top right-hand corner of the screen. It was a message from his boss. He was on standby duty and this could only mean one thing. He was being recalled to duty immediately at the Offices of the Special Advocates in the Palace of Assembly. Nurishad didn't bother to open the message; instead, he prepared to shut down the cuboid. 'Cuboid, deactivate now, please. I'm finished.' Nurishad walked briskly to the door.

'Thank you, Nurishad the Noble. Deactivation is complete. Good day.' The cuboid screen faded to black and readjusted to its original position above the cubicle.

Chapter eight

11:43am Greenwich Meridian Time, 31st August 2022
The Tenth Dimension, the Pure Soul of the universe, Judgment
Chamber in the Palace of Assembly

Young Taifen Kollay was no longer leaning over his mother. Through speaking deep mysteries in the ancient tongue of celestials, the silver cord tying all 23 grams of his soul to his body was released. His body, though, was still in the games room. To Kaithuli, he looked to be in some kind of trance. He was no longer chanting unintelligibly but was completely still.

He was standing inside the stately building of the Palace of Assembly in the City of the Sacred Mountain. Taifen found himself within the entrance of the Judgment Chamber of Argoneo, Lord of the universe. Approximately 20 metres ahead, he was barely able to make out a throne. The golden seat was enveloped in a full white cloud, and there were seven wide golden steps leading up to the gold seat. It emitted waves of white pulsating light which then split into a shimmering rainbow of shades of emerald. The rainbow would shoot upwards to encircle the throne overhead like a halo and drop back down again.

As Taifen gazed intently, his focus cleared. He saw a huge figure seated upon the throne. He was like a man, except his face glistened like jasper mixed with hues of fiery bronze. The figure wore a full-length silken garment with elbow-length sleeves. The gown itself was pure white, matching the snowy locks that framed his face. The lustre of his bare arms made him look as though he had fire trapped in his bones.

Taifen did not know how long he had been standing there before he noticed that on either side of the throne was a semicircle of smaller thrones. There were 12 on the left and 12 on the right. Each throne was crafted from translucent platinum and encrusted with rubies and onyx. The occupants of these smaller thrones were celestial dignitaries dressed in colourful flowing robes. They had silver bands around their waists and silver wreaths on their heads. Moving above all these thrones were four large snow eagles serenading each other.

A small waterfall gushed out of the back of the golden throne. Its water flowed leisurely, like liquid diamond, as if guided within an invisible watercourse in a tidy column down the left side of the throne, rolling neatly over each of the seven wide steps and disappearing into the floor as the water hit the base of the steps.

At the base of the steps were also 12 blazing golden lampstands. Each one was three metres high. They were immaculately arranged and equidistant from each other: six on the right and six on the left. Each lampstand was ornately engraved with images of suns, moons and shooting stars.

For the first time in his short life, Taifen felt as if every cell in his body was ingesting perfectly pure air. His body was throbbing with a pure energy. His heart was drawn towards the great seat by an indescribable mixture of beauty and serenity that streamed towards him. He understood that he was in the presence of perfection. He was overwhelmed. In the same moment, his tear ducts started to fill and he felt bubbles of laughter in his belly floating up to his lips. Taifen bowed deeply before the Lord of the universe. With his head pressed so close to the floor, Taifen was baffled to see that it was constructed from large cubes of clear gold. The gold blocks were so clear that he could see the undulating waves of a gentle flowing river below.

A voice boomed, 'Let the parties in the appeal of the convict Maseray Kollay step forward. The session will commence shortly.'

'Taifen, stand up and follow me,' a voice commanded. Taifen bounced up and raised his head to gaze into the emerald eyes of a man about three metres tall, supremely muscular with unblemished olive skin. His face was exactly symmetrical with perfectly sculpted high cheekbones, a patrician nose, full dark pink lips and a strong chin. His hair, the colour of white gold, hung thick and wavy to his waist. The creature's perfume was an intoxicating mixture of jasmine, aloes and frankincense. Taifen drew a deep breath to savour the heady fragrance. The man flashed a smile to reveal perfectly even teeth. Immaculately dressed in the regalia of an imperial warlord, the stranger was sporting a golden breastplate which contained nine precious stones arranged in three equidistant columns: a ruby, a topaz, a diamond, an emerald, a sapphire and other gemstones that Taifen did not recognise, each one mounted in a setting of solid gold. Engraved in tiny print at the top of his breastplate were the words 'Guardian Cherub'.

'I thought cherubs were chubby little babies that played harps and floated on clouds?' Taifen wondered out loud.

The emerald eyes momentarily flashed with fury. Tossing his long golden hair behind his shoulders, the creature squared them and smoothed his breastplate into place. 'I am a chief underlord of the universe, son of the dawn, ruler of the Earth. You may address me as Zacotan.'

'You are so very beautiful! You must be an angel,' Taifen exclaimed.

'A fallen one: he was stripped of his first estate,' interrupted a voice at Taifen's side. 'I see you are continuing with your age-old strategy of half-truths, Zacotan. You are not the ruler of the Earth. The title deeds to the Earth belong to Lord Argoneo and he has the legal right over everything in it. You have been granted the title "Son of the Dawn", meaning you were the first ever created being, celestial or terrestrial. You *were* the chief underlord of the universe until your status was revoked and you and your allies were cast out of the Tenth Dimension because of your rebelli—'

'Ah, Nurishad the Noble!' interrupted Zacotan with a wide and exaggerated yawn. 'You haven't changed. Forever a stickler for details. Always predictable. infinitely dull. Tell me, old friend, why are you here?'

'I am the Special Advocate assigned to Taifen's mother.'

'Excellent! I could not have wished for a better opponent.' Zacotan smirked and turned to Taifen. 'My dear one, what Nurishad will not want you to know is that over the past 4,000 years, whenever he has appeared as Special Advocate in a trial against me, the appellant lost their appeal – each and every time. All 316 of them are now living in warm subterranean accommodation deep within the core of the First Dimension. Who is peddling half-truths now, O noble Nurishad? What you should be telling Taifen is that he is entitled to make a deal with me.'

'What sort of a deal?' Taifen asked.

'Don't listen to him, Taifen.' Nurishad spoke through gritted teeth. 'He is a liar – the originator of all lies.'

Taifen studied Nurishad for the first time. He was about a metre shorter than Zacotan, with smooth chocolate-brown skin. His piercing sapphire-blue eyes were framed by long black lashes and perfectly trimmed eyebrows. He had shoulder-length black curly hair which seemed an unruly setting for such exquisite features. Nurishad's cream-coloured tunic had wide sleeves and a mulberry sash around the waist. He wore a matching mulberry robe, the vestments of a Special Advocate, with the words 'Equilibrium' and 'Truth' embroidered in gold on the left and right front shoulder panels of the robe.

'Taifen, I have the power to rescue your mother. In the blink of an eye, I can alter her destiny and have her back home with you.' Zacotan opened his palm to reveal a slim, flat, rectangular metallic object. It had a tiny green flashing light in the top right-hand corner. It was a third of the size of a credit card and Taifen recognised it instantly as a *quanta-tablet*. 'Taifen, will you partner with me to make my vision a reality on Earth?' the fallen underlord pleaded softly.

'Is that all? I mean, if I agree to help you build the *quanta-tablet*, my mum will live?'

'It's that simple,' Zacotan confirmed, without meeting Taifen's gaze. Instead, he seemed to be admiring his ring-laden fingers as though seeing their jewels for the first time.

'Don't listen to him, Taifen. The invention of the *quanta-tablet* is the gateway that leads to the fulfilment of an ancient prophecy of the dark ones. It will lead to Lord Argoneo being overthrown, and their rule of the universe at the appointed time: *when the heart of a son of man becomes one with the mind of the son of the dawn.*'

A short flash of lightning straddled the chamber, accompanied by low rumbling thunder. 'I cannot help you, Zacotan,' Taifen replied resolutely.

The mask of indifference fell from Zacotan's features, 'Suit yourself!' he retorted, and hissing slowly he transformed himself into a mighty black, glistening python. Precious jewels and gold studs adorned his head and almost every inch of his thick, fleshy body. Taifen shuddered and stumbled backwards into Nurishad's waiting arms. Zacotan slithered away from them towards the base of the golden steps. When he reached it, he coiled his body upright at the left-hand side of the great throne. Once again, he appeared as a warlord, dressed in his imperial regalia, a model of perfect beauty.

'Court is in session. Let the parties step forward in the case of Maseray Kollay.'

Nurishad smiled warmly at Taifen. 'I am your Special Advocate and have been appointed to represent your mother in this appeal. However, because you summoned the appeal, you still have a choice: I may conduct the case, or if you wish, you may represent your mother.'

'Err… I don't know,' Taifen whispered. 'Zacotan said you've lost every single case you've ever fought with him on the other side!' He could feel his tear ducts filling up. 'How can I trust you with my mother's life?'

'That is true, but you do not know the relevant provisions of the Venerated Edicts. How will you know which arguments of the High Treatise to use? Zacotan will set out a highly legalistic case against your mother. It will be virtually impossible to rebut his arguments. How will you prevail against him when you have not studied the tenets of universal law?'

Taifen looked intently into Nurishad's eyes. 'But you've lost your last 316 cases against Zacotan as prosecutor. That's 316 lives doomed for ever!'

Nurishad lowered his gaze.

'But you are a Special Advocate right?' Nurishad nodded. 'How many appeals have you won in other cases?'

Nurishad shifted his weight from his right to left leg and continued to gaze at his feet.

'Have you ever won an appeal?'

'Not yet.' Nurishad half-smiled, his eyes pleading with Taifen.

Taifen's eyes widened as his lower jaw dropped. 'You mean you have never won a case? Not one single case, and you want me to trust you with my mother's life? Are you crazy?'

'Look, Taifen, I may not have a great track record, but I can help your mother.' Nurishad placed his right hand on Taifen's left shoulder. 'Taifen, the truth is that a Special Advocate is only as good as the facts of the case before him. I can't rewrite history. I can only work with the life history of the person who wants to appeal against their sentence. Sadly, the last 316 cases have been really hopeless. None of them had any chance of winning their appeals.'

Taifen covered his face with both hands, rubbed his temples vigorously and exhaled. 'Aaah! This is crazy. I don't know anything about universal laws, but one thing I do know: only an idiot would go to court without a lawyer. I'm not stupid, even if I am only 12 years old.'

Nurishad beamed. 'One thing I can promise is that when it comes to appeal cases, I know every single code, rule and principle of the universal laws. I'm a great advocate and I will do my best to free your mother.'

Taifen looked around the Judgment Chamber. He was puzzled. Apart from the activity at the front, this huge hall was empty.

'This is an appeal and therefore it is a private hearing, presided over by Lord Argoneo and witnessed by the 12 celestial dignitaries,' Nurishad explained hurriedly. Taifen nodded. Nurishad pointed at a large snow leopard seated behind a gilded desk and chair. 'The court scribe.' Several rolls of parchment, some elegant quills and a crystal inkpot were neatly arranged on the desk. What looked like a small computer was floating about two inches above the middle of the desk.

'Have courage, Taifen. Let us take our places before the Court. The session is about to start.' Nurishad, with Taifen a step behind him, walked quickly towards the right side of the throne. Nurishad bowed deeply and Taifen followed suit. A podium appeared in front of them, rising slowly and effortlessly from the floor.

The announcer spoke: 'Court is now in session.'

Zacotan was already waiting behind his podium. He glanced disdainfully at the unlikely pair, cleared his throat and began his address.

'I, Zacotan, Celestial Prosecutor of the souls of terrestrials, demand that the judgment recorded in the Register of Terrestrials and pronounced over Maseray Kollay be upheld. This is the Venerated Law of the Tenth Dimension.

'It is written in *The Ancient Chronicles of Beings: Celestial and Terrestrial* that each terrestrial has but one lifespan on the Earth. Thereafter, he or she will die at an appointed time. Then each terrestrial will receive judgment according to universal law.' Zacotan paused. He was proud of his knowledge and command of universal law. 'A hundred Earth years ago, Mabinti Sekou, the great-great-great-grandmother of Maseray Kollay, entered into an unbreakable covenant with me. This agreement was sealed with her own blood. In exchange for wealth and riches, she made an oath giving over to me the life of each girl-child in her lineage forever. This started with her own daughter and continues to her children's children's in perpetuity. It is redeemable at any time after the girl-child has lived for 30 Earth years. Maseray Kollay has lived for 35 Earth years. I now tender Exhibit A. Roll the footage, please!' With a flourish of his hand, the air rippled in front of Zacotan and crystallised into a huge rectangular screen.

An image appeared on the screen. It was footage that had been captured on 360-degree celestial cameras of a young girl, tall and slight. She bowed gracefully and then she knelt down in front of a witch doctor. They were in a dark, round hut; the only source of light was the fire blazing brightly between them. To the right of the witch doctor was a wooden statue of a woman, the body of which was concealed by a fleshy mottled-yellow snake that was wrapped around it. The snake's head was resting against the statue's long and heavily beaded neck. Its pink forked tongue occasionally darted out to lightly stroke the beads. At the bottom of the screen, the date was recorded as 9th July 1922, and it recounted the event from the girl's perspective. The witch doctor's face remained hidden, but because the girl was kneeling close to the fire, her heart-shaped face, high cheekbones and small mouth could be seen. Her eyes were lowered and the smooth dark skin on her arms was like melted toffee. She was wearing a once-pretty blue shift dress with a large floral border that was fraying at the hem. The girl wore no shoes and the soles of her feet were chapped and calloused. She bore two keloid scars criss-crossing each other like fat scimitars on her left sole from the arch of her foot all the way to the heel.

'You are here, my child.'

'My father, I pray for wealth and riches in my house.' Mabinti's voice cracked as she swallowed to sink the knot at the base of her throat. 'I am tired of being hungry all the time. Mama says that if we had riches, it would change our lives.'

Mabinti's dress was quivering from the tiny tremors shooting through her skinny body. For the first time in her life she was face to face with the chief priest of the entire Secdelta Region. She had been taught that the chief priest communed face to face with the goddess Shenge. He was the most powerful wizard in the land and he was to be greatly revered. The chief priest was rather more terrifying close up than when she would watch him preside over rituals at the religious festivals and other occasions celebrated by the villagers. Every year, at the eagerly awaited yam festival, Mabinti would witness him cleanly slice off the heads of bulls and goats using the ceremonial swords. The first time she saw him drink the blood of a bull he had just slaughtered, she had been peering through her grandfather's legs. It had left her feeling so queasy that she had not been able to eat anything during the festivities that afternoon. And now, kneeling less than a foot away from him, she was repulsed and excited at the same time.

'What have you brought to trade in exchange for riches?'

'My father, I have nothing.'

'Nothing plus nothing gives nothing. Surely, my child, even you know this.'

Mabinti's lips locked into a steely pout. *If I had money to pay you, I would not be here asking for your help.* She lifted her head and met his gaze defiantly.

'I didn't ask you for money.'

Mabinti gasped softly. Could he read her mind?

The chief priest continued, 'Life is one big marketplace and every man a trader. We buy and we sell. To purchase the secret of wealth you must offer something in exchange. I will ask you again: what have you brought to trade?'

'I have nothing. I own nothing.'

'My daughter, within you lives great power. Only a woman can possess this power. It is the power to bridge the world between the seen and the unseen. To make

something that was invisible appear in flesh and blood…
The power to birth new life.'

Mabinti's mind was spinning. 'You want me to bear your children? I mean, you want me for your wife?'

The chief priest threw his head back, his shoulders heaving as he guffawed. He was savouring her words as if they were the funniest thing he had heard in a long while. He leaned forward, his eyes tiny black coals in a cracked and leathery face. 'No, Mabinti, I do not want a wife. But I do seek the gift of daughters.'

The chief priest was speaking in riddles. Already, Mabinti wished she was back at home, lying on her straw mattress in the safety of their hut, gazing at its mud-baked circular walls. She wondered if he could hear the pounding of her heart in her chest. She felt completely at the mercy of her trembling body, unable to stop herself from shaking. Her dress seemed to possess a mind of its own as it billowed in and out in an erratic rhythm set by her quivering frame. Mabinti clasped her hands tightly in front of her flat belly.

'My father, I am a child and not yet ripe for marriage. Mama says I have to wait for three more rainy seasons and then I will be betrothed to Santiki, son of Melua the antelope hunter. It will be many years before I will have any daughters to give you.'

'I hear you well, my daughter. But we can still trade right now… on a promise for the future. In exchange for the power to gain great riches, you will pledge your daughters' daughters in perpetuity into the service of the goddess Shenge.' The chief priest pointed at the statue with the snake still coiled around it. 'You must promise that as long as there is a girl-child in this lineage, they will serve as her priestesses for ever. Their time of service will only start when your daughters have lived for 30 rainy seasons. Do you accept this?'

'In exchange for riches in my home and the homes of my children's children from now until… until the day the sun falls from the sky.' It was much easier than Mabinti had imagined, and hearing herself repeat the terms of their agreement added to her relief.

'I hear you well, my child. You are a shrewd trader. So let it be done. Wealth and riches shall be in your home from generation to generation or until the day the sun falls from the sky. Now, give me your right hand.'

Mabinti had hardly unclasped her hands when the chief priest reached across and grabbed her right hand. She drew back instantly when she felt a sharp incision along her forefinger but the chief priest did not let go. 'Oooye! My finger.' Mabinti winced as she prised her finger from his grasp. She brought it to her lips, sucking it gently to stop the bleeding.

'Now it is an unbreakable agreement sealed in blood.' The chief priest smiled as he held up the small colourless riverstone that he had used to slice open Mabinti's finger. It was the size of a plum and glistened in the firelight. The chief priest greedily lapped up the blood as it rolled down the sharpened edge of the riverstone. He smacked his lips. Mabinti slowly pulled her finger out of her mouth. Her eyes remained on the chief priest's mouth as his tongue wiped the stone clean. *Is he enjoying licking my blood?*

The chief priest looked up instantly and glared at her. 'Now, my child, go to the river Sewa. Collect as many of these colourless riverstones as you can find. The bigger, the better. In three sunsets, two foreigners will come to your village in search of trade. The chief will turn them away empty-handed. Tell your father to go after them. He must invite them to trade with the riverstones that you have collected. Your family will never be poor again. Now go, but remember that today you have made a solemn promise. From now on your daughters' daughters will serve the goddess Shenge for ever.'

With that, Lethazzar, the fallen celestial and chief priest of Secdelta, vanished. As the yellow snake around the statue of Shenge began to uncoil itself, Mabinti fled the hut.

The screen rippled and disintegrated into thin air.

'And there we have it. History replayed before our very eyes. The records have spoken. Mabinti Sekou and all her daughters from generation to generation are forever my bondslaves, sworn to serve me,' Zacotan spat. 'An unbreakable covenant sealed with blood and witnessed by my faithful cohort, Lethazzar. Maseray Kollay is mine for ever! Or should I say, "until the day the sun falls from the sky".' Zacotan mimicked Mabinti's childish voice. He smiled and spoke softly: 'In short, the prisoner remains in the City of Volcanus and her appeal before this noble Court fails. I rest my case.'

Nurishad stepped forward, bowed low and cleared his throat. 'I stand before this noble Court as Special Advocate representing the prisoner, Maseray Kollay. Her son, Taifen, is present with me. According to the Venerated Law of the Universe, each terrestrial being has but one span of life on Earth. When a mortal reaches the age of awakening, each one must choose where they will draw power for living – either from Lord Argoneo, who is the source of equilibrium, or from Zacotan, Prince of all Dark Illusions. And when every terrestrial dies, he or she draws the sentence of their master and dwells within his abode.' Nurishad paused and turned to Zacotan. 'However, there have been exceptions to this rule. There are cases where a terrestrial has died but has been revived to live again. This is because that terrestrial received an extension of time to their lifespan. In other words, that terrestrial has gained added years.

'For example, in 2014, Verdiano Luigi Perezzi, a celebrated terrestrial film star, died in a car crash. He was pronounced dead at the scene of the accident and the incident was beamed into the homes of millions of viewers by satellite TV. Yet, 67 minutes after he died, Verdiano was brought back to life in a hospital. He had received an extension of time to dwell on the Earth. There are several other examples of this in human history, including Professor Dadgo, a leading scholar in the field of applied mathematics in 2017. There was also—'

'Objection!' Zacotan growled. 'These examples are all totally irrelevant and inadmissible in this case. Neither of those two people had entered into a blood covenant to be my bondslaves in exchange for riches from me.' Zacotan stared pointedly at the gold lettering on the right side of Nurishad's robe. 'Isn't that the *truth*?' Nurishad glanced down at his right shoulder. The word 'Truth' shone back at him. He felt a tug at the back of his robe and turned around. Taifen wanted to speak to him.

'Is there a law that can give my mother another lifespan?' he whispered.

'Well, er, no. I mean yes! I'm not sure. There is a rule that could help, but I don't know if we will be able to use it,' Nurishad whispered back.

'Why not?'

'It's too risky.'

'I don't care. Tell me about this law,' Taifen scowled.

Nurishad sighed. 'There is a provision in universal law which states that for every terrestrial being there shall be an exact prescription of length of days allotted to them by the members of the Supreme High Council on which Lord Argoneo sits. It appears to be connected to maintaining a kind of equilibrium in our worlds, but no one knows with certainty. The law states that no terrestrial shall be told in advance the number of days that have been allotted to him or her to live on the Earth. Nonetheless, each terrestrial is expected to spend every day purposefully. So I believe that you can argue a case, in theory, that one terrestrial is permitted to give up a portion of their days on the Earth to another. Those days could then be deducted from the donor's life and credited to the recipient's life and equilibrium will be maintained. So, if we apply this to your case, your mother can be given added years to live on the Earth, but this extra time must come from someone else. Another terrestrial would have to give up a portion of their days on the Earth. Those days could then be credited to your mother's lifespan. The final result would be that she would live again on the Earth.'

It took a moment for the weight of Nurishad's words to register in Taifen's brain. As they did so, his chest began to hurt. It felt like a pair of invisible hands were at work on him. One hand was pressing against his heart. The other was squeezing the air passage in his throat. He needed to process things quickly because his legs were beginning to wobble. If he gave up some of his days on Earth to his mother then she would receive those days as a new lifespan. She would come back home to them. But then his own life would be cut short. *I don't want to die before my time! I want to live!*

Nurishad cleared his throat softly, 'Dear one, you need to know that any added years from you will not deliver your mother from this fatal bargain with Zacotan. It can only buy precious time for your mother to return to Earth and give her the opportunity to seek complete freedom with the help of Lord Argoneo. He alone has the power to break Zacotan's stranglehold permanently over your family.'

Taifen nodded: he wasn't able to reply. Like his father, he had already taken an oath of allegiance to Argoneo, and their future in the Tenth Dimension was secure. It was not so for Maseray or Kaithuli. In this moment, standing in the Judgment Chamber, nothing mattered to him except that his beloved mother should be allowed to return home. Above all, he wanted her to have the opportunity once more to renounce Zacotan and to embrace life in Argoneo.

Zacotan's voice cut into Taifen's thoughts. 'My Lord Argoneo, this is unacceptable. Nurishad the Noble is holding up the session. This is no time for chit-chat!' Zacotan's voice was barely a decibel short of a scream.

'My Lord, Noble Council,' Nurishad bowed low, 'may I crave your kind indulgence whilst I confer with the prisoner's son?'

'Objection! Time is of the essence and this case must proceed at once or be dismissed immediately.' The veins in Zacotan's neck were swollen thick.

'Your objection is denied. You will suffer no prejudice from a momentary pause. Nurishad, be swift.' Lord Argoneo had given his ruling and Nurishad turned to Taifen. Before he could say anything, Taifen blurted out, 'I've made up my mind. I will give ten years of my life to my mother.'

'Taifen! You are far too young! Do you really know what you are doing? This is a very serious matter. No one but the three members of the Supreme High Council knows how long anybody will live. Your entire destiny could be altered if you were to die prematurely.'

'My mother is coming home,' Taifen snapped fiercely, tears spilling down his cheeks. He had a choice to make but in his heart it felt like no choice at all; he wanted Maseray back home with them. Suddenly he noticed that his tongue felt very dry and the back of his throat hurt. He knew he had just been given enough ink to rewrite his family's destiny, but it came at a great cost. *This is so unfair! I don't want to die before my time.* To stop himself from changing his mind, Taifen pushed hurriedly past Nurishad. He stepped into the space between the two podiums. The young terrestrial knelt before Lord Argoneo and the Council of celestial dignitaries. With his head back, eyes closed and both arms fully extended in front of him, the small human child sang in the language of the Tenth Dimension:

Parra o semo lema kara, Sefero mo keare pasha
Selimi maketerra pazulu kutelu si ti re.

Parra o semo lema kara, Tefleo negero beli bela
Selimi maketerra pazulu kutelu si ti re.
Cerreo salith kosa mona, Tefleo negero beli bela
Selimi maketerra pazulu kutelu si ti re dos si.

Taifen's plea started as a groan and grew into a sorrowful melody that filled the huge chamber. As he drew breath to sing each note, he was infused with Argoneo's great love. It flowed from Argoneo to him, filling his lungs and coursing through his body. It was a rush of energy, strengthening his resolve to give up a portion of his days to facilitate his mother's return. It was his decision, but it was the strength that came with being in Argoneo's presence that enabled him to stick to it. A melancholy quiet fell upon the room. He repeated his refrain and lowered his head on the last note. Breaths and bodies were quietened to silence. No one moved as they waited for the boy's petition to be answered by the Lord of the universe. The celestial dignitaries had observed Taifen keenly: his eyes had glittered with a fierce resolve. He had no way of knowing that he had displayed to them an uncommon courage that was found in very few, terrestrial or celestial.

Lord Argoneo's deep, clear voice called those assembled back to order. It was like the sound of a deep, rushing ocean. 'Young terrestrial, Son of Maseray Kollay, the Council and I accept your request for an exchange of life between you and your mother. The sacrifice will be for five, not ten, years of your life. Therefore, your mother will be credited with an additional length of 1,826 days to live on the Earth. Your own life on Earth is hereby reduced by precisely the same number of days. The time will run immediately.'

'This is outrageous, my Lord Argoneo! What about the acknowledgment of debt, signed and sealed with the blood of the prisoner's ancestor? I have the document right here!' Zacotan waved a sheet of paper wildly in front of him. As he did so, the smooth skin on his face began to turn scaly. His eyes grew even larger, bulging out of their sockets. 'The lineage of Mabinti Sekou's daughters are pledged to my service from generation to generation! I can demand their presence with me in Volcanus any time after the age of 30. It is my right!' He struck a fist down heavily on the podium before him.

'Ah yes,' Nurishad piped up. 'But you forget that under the doctrine of the supremacy of life, the force of life always supersedes the force of death. Where a life is laid down as a willing sacrifice for another, the power of life displaces death and breaks all binding ties, including blood ties. And equilibrium is maintained in the universe. Today, you have been silenced by the song of a child.'

'I demand justice! She belongs to me!' Zacotan screamed, revealing a pink forked tongue. 'Maseray Kollay is mine!' By now, his limbs were completely covered in thick charcoal black scales, and a charcoal snake-tail hissed viciously behind him.

'I have given my verdict and justice is well served,' Lord Argoneo replied. 'The Venerated Principle of a life for a life cannot be overturned. Special Advocate Nurishad has spoken rightly. Let this judgment now be recorded: Taifen Kollay has released 1,826 days of his lifespan on the Earth in exchange for a credit of an equal length of such days to his mother, Maseray. The blood covenant between Zacotan and the forebear of Maseray Kollay is suspended for 1,826 days. So as it is written in the Tenth Dimension, let it be done in all other nine.'

The large snow leopard, who had sat silently as a scribe throughout the proceedings, stood up to broadcast the judgment.

◆ † ◆

11:50am Greenwich Meridian Time, 31st August 2022
In the City of Volcanus, the First Dimension, the Dark Soul of
the Universe

The announcement came out of the blue and sounded sharply in the cubicle: 'It is this day recorded that the appeal on behalf of Maseray Kollay is successful under the Venerated Law of Just Recompense. By virtue of the free will offering given by Taifen Kollay, there will be a reduction of his lifespan upon the Earth of 1,826 days in exchange for an equal credit to be added to the lifespan of Maseray Kollay. The prisoner is hereby released.'

As soon as the announcement ended, a small shaft of white light appeared in the cubicle. The light expanded and rippled throughout the cubicle before settling into tiny waves of rainbow colours. A figure of a man took shape within the light. Maseray knew intuitively who it was. 'My Lord Argoneo,' she whispered as she fell on her face, trembling. She felt a huge roll of energy stream from Lord Argoneo towards her. She could not fully define the substance of what was being transmitted to her, and she could only liken it to billows of tranquillity. A tangible peace. She let it wash over her body, sinking deep into her pores, swirling through her insides, cooling her heart, caressing her soul. Each roll was pushing out of her body the physical memory of pain and grief over the loss of her mother, Aunty Symchee, her many cousins and aunts. Her muscles were relaxing and with that, tears began to slip down her face.

Lord Argoneo was speaking to her: 'My precious one, I have granted the petition of your son, Taifen. I am extending exceptional grace to you by permitting you to return to Earth to live again. Taifen's sacrificial act does not break the curse of premature death over you. Zacotan's claim to your life is only suspended and it remains valid and effective. For no terrestrial has the power to nullify Zacotan's power. That power resides in me alone. Be strong and courageous: I have set you on the path to freedom, and as you seek after me you will find it. On the Earth, things are not always as they seem. You must remember to look beyond the mere appearance of things.'

Chapter nine

The curtain between life and death parted. Maseray stepped through it from eternity back into time. As her soul re-entered her body, she started to shiver. It was an involuntary response to the contrast between the searing heat in the cubicle in Volcanus and the fresh, cool air in the family games room.

She remained on her back on the carpet with her eyes closed and fought to gather her thoughts. Somewhere in the distance, she could hear the sound of a siren drawing close. She was too scared to open her eyes in case she found herself back in the cubicle. A loud crash made her sit up and start to breathe again. The lampstand of Shenge had struck the floor, face forward. Shenge's head was cracked open and a large split was running from the peak of her forehead down through the length of her torso.

Someone was banging on their front door. The visitor was also pressing the doorbell rapidly. At the same time, a male voice joined the cacophony. He was shouting Kaithuli's name. Maseray struggled to clear her mind. Taifen, who was kneeling behind her, had come out of his trance and wrapped his small arms tightly around her. He pressed his right cheek against her back. He felt as though his heart would burst with joy. Taifen raised his head and kissed Maseray's back three times. Again, he placed his right cheek against her back and tightened his embrace. Taifen was humming. Maseray felt her body slowly warm as her heart picked up its normal pace, slotting back into her life's rhythm.

Relief had hardly washed over Maseray when it was immediately replaced by a dull pain in her chest. *Alive.* But at great cost. Taifen had laid down a segment of his lifespan so that she would live again. *My baby – what has he done?* She put her face in her hands and wept. *No, I won't allow Taifen's life to be cut short. I will seek out Lord Argoneo, there must be another way.* Maseray's lips were moving rapidly yet silently as she muttered under her breath. *I have lived my whole life not knowing that Argoneo is kind, good and without injustice. I will tell him that my eyes are now open and I see that he is light and that there is no darkness in him. It is Zacotan who is our enemy, full of hatred and evil. I will take an oath of allegiance to Argoneo. I have been in his presence and I can't go back to the way things were.*

Maseray continued to weep softly. Taifen assumed that they were tears of joy. He squeezed her even more tightly, pressing his cheek against his mother's back. She was home now, and he felt strongly that there had to be a way to break permanently the power of this darkness over their family. The answer was with Argoneo, and they would find it. Today was her birthday. They would be celebrating his own in just a few days' time. Taifen's lips broadened into a wide smile as he started to sing softly, 'Happy Birthday to us, Happy Birthday to us...'

Kaithuli was staring at his mother, wide-eyed. He took a couple of deep breaths and could feel the muscles in his neck and shoulders begin to relax. He wasn't sure if he should hug her or if he should sit patiently and wait for her to stop sobbing. Perhaps he would wait for Taifen to release her from his embrace. He could see that Taifen had got over his shock and was himself again.

The banging on their front door had not lessened, and the person was still screeching his name. Kaithuli rose mechanically, almost in slow motion. 'I'll get the door. It's the ambulance people…' he said, walking backwards, unable to take his eyes off his mother.

Epilogue

Offices of the Special Advocates
Court of the Tenth Dimension in the Palace of Assembly
In the Pure Soul of the Universe

Nurishad had requested a copy of the scroll containing the judgment in the case of Maseray Kollay. It was the first appeal he had ever won and he wanted the scroll framed and displayed in pride of place on the wall behind his desk. As he perused the document for the fourth time, he heard footsteps approaching. There was a knock at his door.

'Enter!'

A short, fat, bird-like celestial entered, carrying a golden platter. He had a smooth face with a ruddy complexion. The rest of his body was covered in white and black feathers with golden tips. His round tawny eyes were smiling as he bowed. He was Nurishad's loyal and trusted personal attendant. He placed a crystal goblet containing the juice of freshly pressed aloes and a small bowl of jacqoi berries on his master's desk. 'Refreshments, Sir?' A small silver envelope was also on the gold platter and he extended it to Nurishad.

'I hear congratulations are in order, Sir. The terrestrial's appeal was successful.'

'Thank you, Qunu,' Nurishad sighed. The truth that it was a partial victory, buying priceless time for Maseray Kollay. But he was not going to let that stop him from savouring this moment. He would remain hopeful about Maseray's future.

Nurishad turned the envelope over to open it. He recognised the emerald seal. All missives from the City of Volcanus carried it. He removed a small white sheet from the envelope. It read:

From: Zacotan, chief underlord of the universe
Ruler of Volcanus, Son of the Dawn

To: Nurishad the Noble
Special Advocate of the Tenth Dimension

Maseray Kollay belongs to me. Do not think otherwise.
For the day is coming, indeed, it is already upon us, when the heart of a son of man becomes one with the mind of the son of the dawn.
You have won this battle, but you will not win the war.

Nurishad shook his head as he folded the note and replaced it in the envelope. 'I trust all is well, Sir?' Qunu quizzed.

'Well enough, my dear.' Nurishad placed the envelope on his desk. 'This is Zacotan's attempt to strike fear in our hearts, but on the contrary, I am not moved. I have every hope that Maseray Kollay and all those in the dynasty of Mabinti Sekou will be rescued from his clutches.'

Qunu's curiousity was aroused. 'How so, Sir?'

'Mabinti Sekou entered into a deadly covenant through an oath of allegiance that she made to Zacotan masquerading as the goddess Shenge. She gave Zacotan legal right to cut short the life of every woman descended from her. In the same way, any female member of

Mabinti's dynasty can revoke the covenant by entering into a covenant with a higher power.'

'This is very good news. If I understand you correctly, Sir, you are saying that Maseray Kollay is entitled to revoke the covenant with Zacotan.' Qunu fluffed his feathers.

'Precisely. If she makes an oath to faithfully serve Argoneo, then all legal rights granted to Zacotan over her life and the lives of her descendants will be revoked. She should then live a long and healthy life. This whole experience has taught her many things, and she is already beginning to seek after Lord Argoneo. Taifen's sacrifice has given her a window of opportunity, but it cannot release her from bondage to Zacotan. No terrestrial is qualified to do so. She must look to Lord Argoneo now, for he alone has the power to repudiate the curse over her life and rescue her from the clutches of Zacotan. She has endured much sorrow in her 35 years, and now things are coming into perfect alignment for Maseray's liberation.'

'And besides, she has 1,826 days to do so,' Qunu smiled.

'Indeed, and she has Cho and Taifen to guide her.' Nurishad popped a jacqoi berry into his mouth. 'These events, as traumatic as they have been, could also be the impetus that Kaithuli, the older son, needs to encourage him to consider taking an oath of allegiance to Lord Argoneo'.

'That would be a most splendid outcome for this family'.

'Indeed.'

'Will that be all, Sir?'

'That will be all, thank you.'

Qunu bowed and waddled to the door. Nurishad turned to face his computer. He would begin to prepare a list of legal authorities on the principle of the power of life and death exercised through allegiance. He was expecting a request for help imminently from a member of the Kollay family. It would be in one of the languages of celestials in the Tenth Dimension – and he hoped that it would come from Maseray.

Note to readers

The Ancient Chronicles of Beings: Celestial and Terrestrial does not exist. It is a complete figment of the imagination designed to bring cohesion to the story, and there was no discovery of any such text in Timbuktoo at any time. On the other hand, Nachmanides is a revered philosopher who espoused his beliefs on the existence of the ten dimensions in the universe. His beliefs remain subject to scholarly debate.